READ LEFT TO RIGHT

HAH...
H-HELP...
Bella Diamante
HELP ME...

MAPLE BOULEVARD
NOVEMBER
16TH 2017

AHEM.
TAP

HELLO MR MASOMILIO. THIS IS NIGHTSHADE.

SO YOU FINALLY CAME RIGHT TO THE TOP.

TOYING WITH AMATEURS WAS FUN AT THE TIME BUT ULTIMATELY LACKED STIMULATION.
HOW IS LIFE WITHOUT YOUR ACE TEAM OF HACKERS BY THE WAY?
IF YOU MEAN TO IMPLY THAT YOU SLEW THEM ALL, YOU HAVEN'T FINISHED THE JOB.
I BEG TO DIFFER. THE *TALENTED* ONES ARE DEAD AND THAT LEAVES CONTROL OF EVERYTHING IN MY HANDS.
TELL ME THEN, WHAT EXACTLY DOES CONTROLLING *EVERYTHING* ENTAIL?

I CAN SEE. HEAR. TRACE.OCCUPY AND KILL ANYONE. ANYTHING. ANY-WHERE. ANY-TIME.
AND THERE'S NO WAY OF TAKING THAT CONTROL FROM ME EVEN IF I DIE.

WHAT COULD YOU POSSIBLY WANT FROM ME THEN?
SIMPLE: COMPLIANCE.

HMM...

MS MATSUI, I AM A MAN WITH CONSIDERABLY MORE RESOURCES THAN ANYONE YOU'VE EVER ENCOUNTERED...
IT MAY BE UNWISE TO TEST THAT SORT OF POWER.

"POWER" YOU SAY? POOR CHOICE OF WORDS. YOU NEED TO TALK LESS AND LISTEN *CLOSELY* NOW..

I AM NO MERE HACKER SIR. I AM THE *SOURCE.*

THE *COMMANDS* REST IN MY *VEINS.*

THAT'S ABSURD...

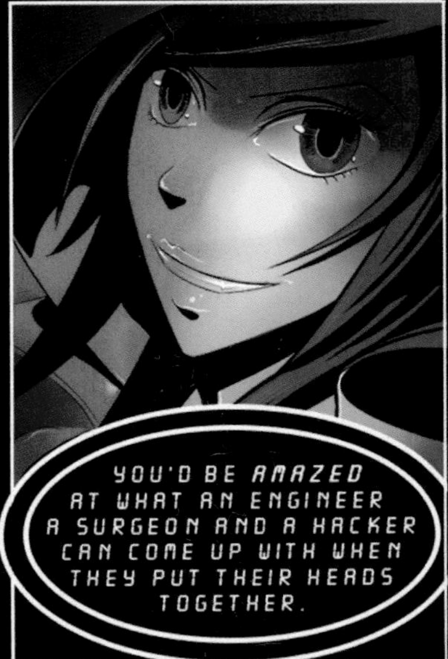

YOU'D BE *AMAZED* AT WHAT AN ENGINEER A SURGEON AND A HACKER CAN COME UP WITH WHEN THEY PUT THEIR HEADS TOGETHER.

AND YET ALL YOU NEED IS A PSYCH-IATRIST.
OH YES! IT'S THANKS TO A PSYCHIATRIST I'M NO LONGER IN PRISON! SHE DIDN'T LIKE ME MUCH THOUGH...
NO? I CAN'T IMAGINE WHY...
COCKY AREN'T YOU? YOUR POOR WIFE WON'T KNOW WHAT HIT HER.
WAIT-
NO NO. IF PROOF IS WHAT YOU NEED PROOF IS WHAT YOU SHALL HAVE.
SHE'LL BE DRIVING YOUR SONS HOME FROM THEIR CONCERT ABOUT NOW. CORRECT?

THERE'S NO NEED TO-
BOOM

I TOLD YOU DIDN'T I? YOU TALK TOO MUCH.
WHAT HAVE YOU DONE?
WELL FIRST I CUT OFF THE CITY'S POWER & DATA NETWORK BUT YOU SEEMED A LITTLE OBNOXIOUS SO I DETONATED THE EXPLOSIVES IN YOUR WIFE'S CAR.
KILLING FAMILIES AND DE-STROYING PROPERTY DOESN'T GET YOU COMPLIANCE IT GETS YOU HUNTED!
AHH... RELAX. YOUR FAMILY EXITED THE VEHICLE A LITTLE WHILE AGO.
...BUT YOU DO OWE YOUR WIFE A NEW CAR.

YOU SEE *SIR:* MY THREATS ARE NEVER HOLLOW AND WITH THAT IN MIND...

I'D LIKE YOU TO IMAGINE HOW *AWFUL* IT WOULD BE IF UPTOWN AND DOWNTOWN SOMEHOW *SPILLED INTO ONE ANOTHER.*

QUIET *NOW* HUH.

DOWNTOWN IS-
NOT UNDER YOUR JURISDICTION. I KNOW. DOWNTOWN IS *MINE.*

SO IF YOU WOULD LIKE TO BE ENEMIES RATHER THAN ALLIES IT CAN BE ARRANGED...

BUT IF YOU CAN'T EVEN GET THE LIGHTS BACK ON I'D BE SERIOUSLY WORRIED ABOUT WHAT ELSE I CAN DO TO YOU.

IT'S YOUR MOVE!
CLICK
SIR?
MEET ME IN THE SITUATION ROOM.
RIGHT NOW? YOU DO KNOW THE TIME RIGHT?

OH, DON'T MIND ME, I'LL JUST PUT THIS THREAT TO NATIONAL SECURITY ON ICE UNTIL YOU'RE *WELL-RESTED* SHALL I?
...
I'LL BE THERE IN FIVE.
WAKE UP THE MAN IN THE BOX ON YOUR WAY OVER.
...
R-REALLY?
REALLY.

I FEEL
I SHOULD
WISH YOU ALL
GOOD LUCK...
...AND SAY
I'M *TERRIBLY*
SORRY FOR WHAT'S
ABOUT TO HAPPEN...
...BUT WHAT'S
THE POINT OF
LYING WHEN YOU
CAN'T EVEN
HEAR ME!?

LET THERE BE MAYHEM.

X2

ONE YEAR LATER...

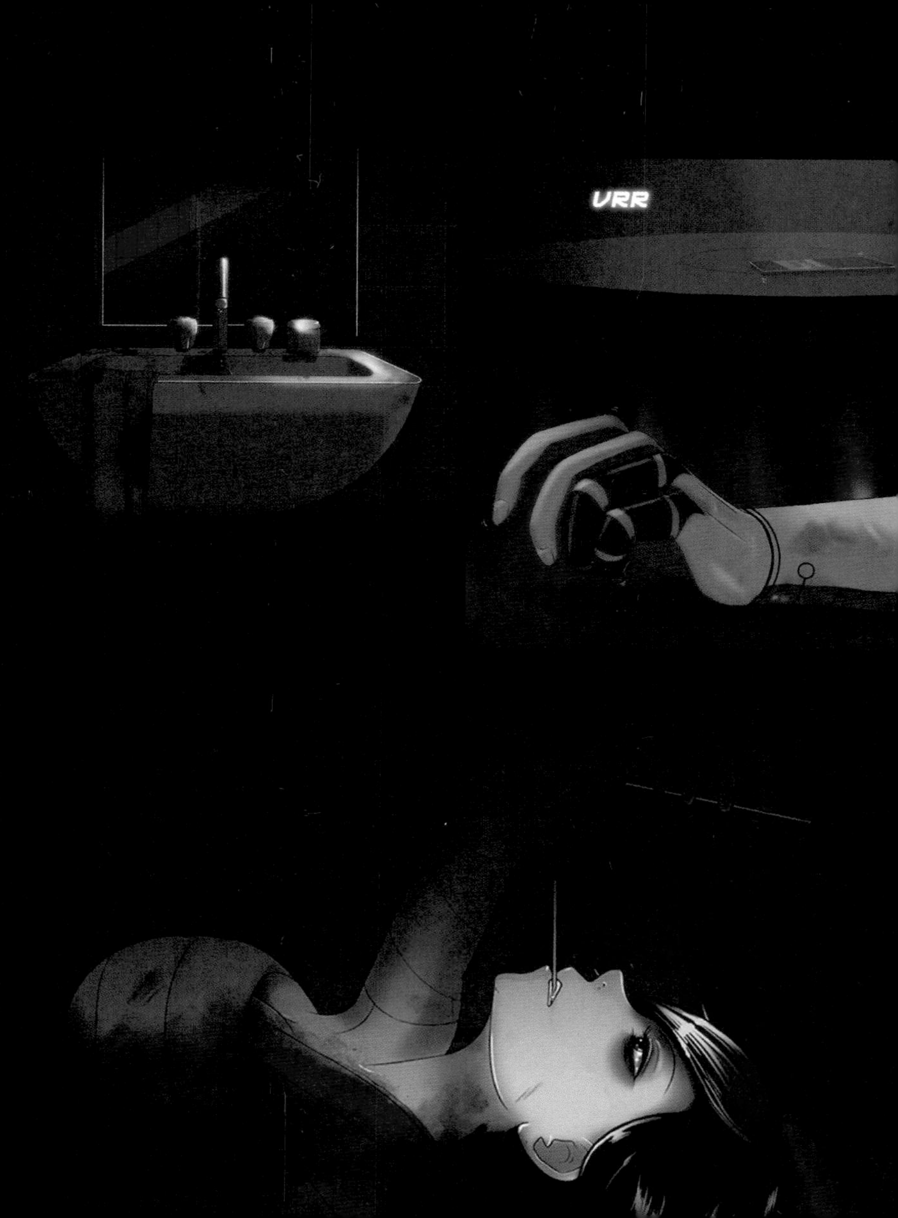
VRR

TCH...
THAT'S MY TRICK.
VRR
Number Unavailable

HELLO
BELLA.

THIS IS
NIGHTSHADE

HELLO.

VOLUME 3

Written and Illustrated by
Hanna Rose

Special thanks to my Patrons Peter, Dave, Simone, Lynne, Gareth, Haden, Jacob & Sheridan, as well as my partner and close friends.
You have all made this alongside me.

All characters, names, places and events within this book are fictional creations of the author's mind. Any resemblance to actual persons, (living or dead) events or places is purely coincidental.

CONTENTS

PTER 1: RELAPSE

Hope you enjoyed the prologue chapter! The events of this book take place after the Bella - Masomilio scene but before the fast forward section. In fact, everything you saw after the fast forward (including the final scene which we will catch up with eventually) takes place in the series ahead. The date is March 2018, four years on from the end of Volume Two...

NOBODY IN THIS GAME IS WITHOUT AN ENEMY.

SOME OPERATE ALONE, OTHERS IN GROUPS.

YOUR ENEMY MIGHT BE WORKING FOR YOUR FRIEND...
...AND YOUR FRIEND MAY TRY TO KILL YOU.
BECAUSE THIS GAME IS BIGGER THAN YOU OR ME...
...IT IS BIGGER THAN THIS BROKEN CITY...
...THIS GAME CAN ONLY BE WON BY ONE.
BUT TELL ME...

DO ANY OF US REALLY KNOW WHAT WE'RE PLAYING FOR?

OLIVER, IS THAT YOU?
YEAH.
COME HERE A MINUTE.
WHAT'S UP?

...iller escapes high security facility

...s criminal is on the run from authorities following a violent ... from Aspen High Security Prison Facility. The woman, 22, ...ecorded by security cameras fleeing the prison grounds having murdered 5 inmates and 3 prison officials before making her escape in the guise of Dr Penelope Casey, 38, a highly respected criminal psychologist who was killed in the escape.

On 3rd March 2015 the woman pleaded guilty to the shooting of Asare Fullinger and Benjamin Sloane and was sentenced to ten years in prison.

Superintendent Austin Hudson said: "Footage indicates that this was a premeditated escape plan with a total disregard for the loss of life involved. We are devoting our full attention to the swift containment of the criminal."

Anyone who may have information regarding the escapee is advised to call their local police authority, and is expressly warned to avoid direct confrontation.

Guilty as charged - Jailed for murder at just 18 years of age.

...hting - as seen

MY GRAND-FATHER WAS AN INSPIRATION TO MANY, MYSELF INCLUDED.
...BUT SIX YEARS AGO, HE WAS *SHOT.*
THE SIDE OF HIM I NEVER KNEW WAS THAT OF AN EMINENT COMPUTER SCIENTIST WORKING WITH THE GOVERNMENT.
AND HIS KILLER WAS ***NIGHTSHADE***; A HACKER WHO CONTROLLED THE ENTIRE GHETTO WITH BLOODY THREATS AND MANIPULATION....
IN COMPARISON, *I* WAS A SHELTERED 16 YEAR OLD BOY WHO DIDN'T EVEN REALISE THERE WERE PEOPLE *LIVING* IN THAT PLACE.
I SET OUT TO IDENTIFY NIGHTSHADE 2 YEARS AFTER THE SHOOTING WITH NO CLUE HOW DRAMATICALLY IT WOULD CHANGE MY LIFE.

NEEDLESS TO SAY; I NEEDED HELP. THAT'S WHEN I MET BELLA. SHE KNEW THE STREETS AND KEPT ME ALIVE.
IT NEVER CROSSED MY MIND THAT A PERSON I CARED FOR SO MUCH COULD BE NIGHTSHADE.
SHE WENT SO FAR AS TO *MURDER* ONE OF MY FRIENDS AND STAGE AN ATTACK ON HERSELF THAT COST HER TWO FINGERS & NEARLY HER LIFE; ***ALL TO KEEP ANYONE FROM UNCOVERING HER IDENTITY.***
SHE EVEN ***STABBED*** KAI, HER CLOSEST FRIEND, AND LEFT HIM FOR DEAD. FORTUNATELY, HE WAS FOUND AND MANAGED TO SURVIVE.

THE MOMENT I LEARNED THE TRUTH, I WAS SO ANGRY I CALLED EVERY VICIOUS CRIMINAL SHE'D EVER ABUSED AND TOLD THEM EXACTLY WHO SHE REALLY WAS.
WHAT FOLLOWED WAS A GRUELLING NIGHT OF VIOLENCE WHICH TRANS-FORMED DOWNTOWN INTO A BATTLEFIELD, COST COUNTLESS LIVES AND LEFT LASTING SCARS ON ALL THOSE PRESENT.
BUT KAI DIDN'T AGREE WITH MY METHODS, HE RISKED HIS LIFE AND QUIT HIS GANG TO KEEP HER ALIVE SO SHE COULD BE ARRESTED INSTEAD.
THOUGH IT ONLY SCRATCHED THE SURFACE OF HER CRIMES, SHE PLEADED GUILTY TO MANSLAUGHTER AND MURDER, WHICH EARNED HER A TEN YEAR PRISON SENTENCE.

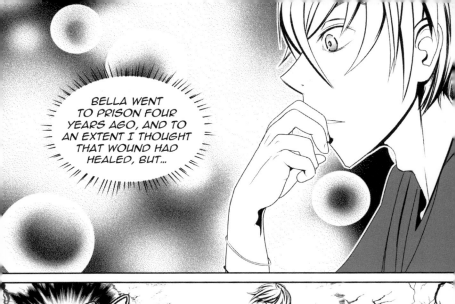

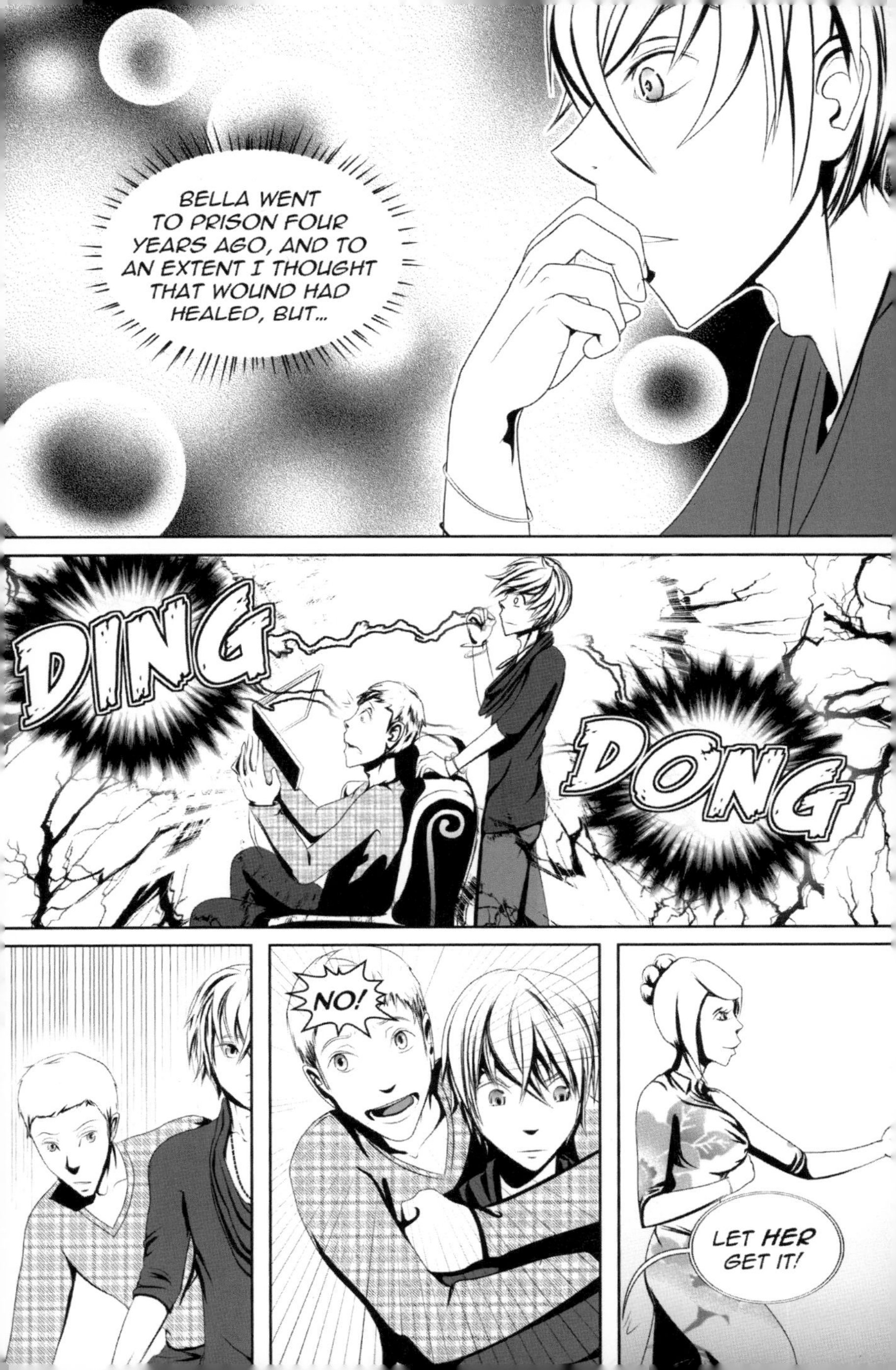

BELLA WENT TO PRISON FOUR YEARS AGO, AND TO AN EXTENT I THOUGHT THAT WOUND HAD HEALED, BUT...

DING
DONG

NO!

LET HER GET IT!

THAT'S A
TERRIBLE
ATTITUDE!!

WELL...
SHE PROBABLY
WOULDN'T DIE
RIGHT AWAY.

NO, YOU'RE
HOPING IT TAKES
LONG ENOUGH FOR
YOU TO RUN OUT
THE BACK...

EXCUSE ME,
ARE YOU MRS.
SLOANE?
I AM.
WE WOULD
LIKE TO SPEAK
TO YOUR SON.

WHAT HAVE
YOU BEEN UP
TO NOW?

NOTHING!

THAT'S THE ONE. BRING HIM IN.

OLIVER SLOANE, WE BELIEVE YOU ARE AT RISK AND IT IS OUR DUTY TO PROTECT YOU. WOULD YOU PLEASE COME WITH US?
FIRST SHOW ME SOME ID. THEN I'LL THINK ABOUT PACKING MY BAGS.

HOW CAN YOU BE SO CALM ABOUT IT?! ARE WE REALLY RELATED?
APOLOGIES FOR THE INTRUSION, BUT

I UNDER-STAND YOU ARE FAMILIAR WITH NIGHTSHADE...
SHE HAS BEEN ENACTING A MALICIOUS PLAN. WE ARE HERE TO PROTECT YOU FROM HER, BUT WE CANNOT AFFORD TO WASTE TIME.

WHAT IS HER PLAN?

IT WOULD BE UNWISE TO GO INTO THOSE DETAILS RIGHT NOW.
THANK YOU FOR THE CONCERN, BUT IF YOU CAN'T PROTECT THE WHOLE OF MY FAMILY-

THERE IS NO REASON TO BELIEVE SHE WILL HARM YOUR FAMILY.
TRUST ME, SHE IS **NOT** ABOVE A DIRTY TACTIC LIKE THAT!
HEHE**HE'S** NOT CLEAN **AT ALL!**

THINGS LIKE THAT DON'T HAPPEN IN THIS CITY. STANDARD ENFORCEMENT WILL BE SUFFICIENT FOR YOUR FAMILY.
GO WITH THEM OLIVER.

MOM!
IF THAT GIRL COMES BACK IT'S YOU SHE'LL GO FOR. *HERE.*
THIS SHOULD BE EVERYTHING YOU NEED.
THAT WAS *FAST!!*

SERIOUSLY, I'M NOT GOING TO LEAVE YOU BEHIND!
YOU WANNA GET KILLED?!
GAH! BY HER OR YOU?!
GET OUT!
SORRY.
YOU'D BETTER BRING HIM BACK IN ONE PIECE. HE'S 20 AND HASN'T HAD A SINGLE GIRLFRIEND YET!
MOM!?
YOU CAN'T ATTACK A MAN'S PRIDE LIKE THAT!!
I WANT GRANDKIDS.

GEHEH...
I TAKE IT BACK, CLEAN AS A WHISTLE! HOW'D THIS FOOL GET MIXED UP WITH DOWNTOWN?
HE SHOULD'VE BEEN VETTED YEARS AGO.

WHAT THE HELL?
WHO **SAYS** THINGS LIKE THAT??
LIKE WHAT?
LIKE **"VETTED"** YOU FREAK! WHO'S **VETTING** THE KID? YOU?
IT WAS AN EXPRESSION.

I DON'T LIKE YOU MILANO.
SO YOU KEEP SAYING.

THAT SHOULD SCARE YOU.

AUTHORITY IS NOTHING TO FEAR.

YOU WON'T LAST LONG WITH AN ATTITUDE LIKE THAT.

WHAT'S HE DOING NOW?
I THINK SOMEONE'S SLASHED YOUR TYRES.
SWOOSH

OLIVER!!

IS THAT
...HIM?
YOU KNOW
ANYONE ELSE
WHO DRIVES
LIKE THAT?

THUD
OW!
!?
NUGH!!

THEY'RE RIGHT ON OUR TAIL. FOUR VEHICLES IN TOTAL...
...AND THEY'LL ALL BE ARMED.
SKREECH

HEADS DOWN!
FWAP
TRICKY...
IF WE TAKE THE NEXT LEFT WE CAN SHAKE THEM OFF DOWN MAPLE BOULEVARD.
YOU WANT ME TO DRIVE DOWN A MAIN ROAD?
YES! LEFT! NOW!
I SAID: LEFT!!
NO!

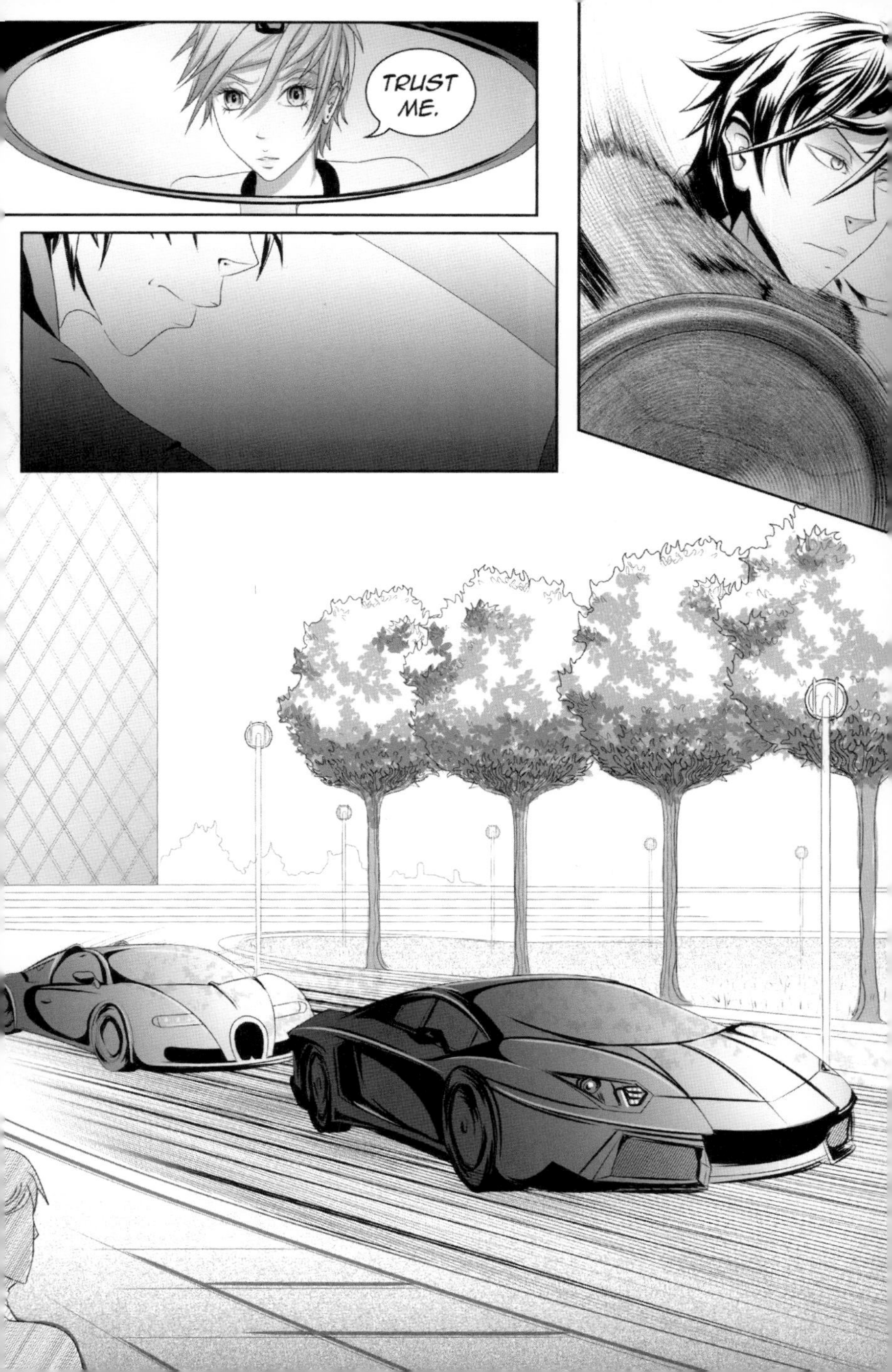
TRUST ME.

RIGHT DOWN THE HIGH STREET? WHAT'S HE TRYING TO PULL?
I TOLD YOU: HIS LITTLE NAVIGATOR IS HELPING HIM TO SHAKE US OFF.
WELL...
HIS LITTLE NAVIGATOR SORELY UNDERESTIMATES A HUNTER.
REMAIN IN PURSUIT.
SIR, THAT WOULD TAKE US RIGHT THROUGH THE CITY CENTRE...
YES. IT WOULD.
BUT WE CAN'T-
I SAID REMAIN IN PURSUIT!!
MAPLE BOULEVARD

DAMN, I DIDN'T THINK THEY'D COME DOWN HERE...
WHY NOT?! WE CAN'T OUTRUN HIM IN A STRAIGHT LINE, I'VE *TOLD YOU* THIS!!
WOOOOOO
POLICE
HAHA! LOOK AT HER STARING ME DOWN!
SMYTHE! THE POLICE-
SHUT UP AND SHOOT HIS TYRES OUT.
BANG

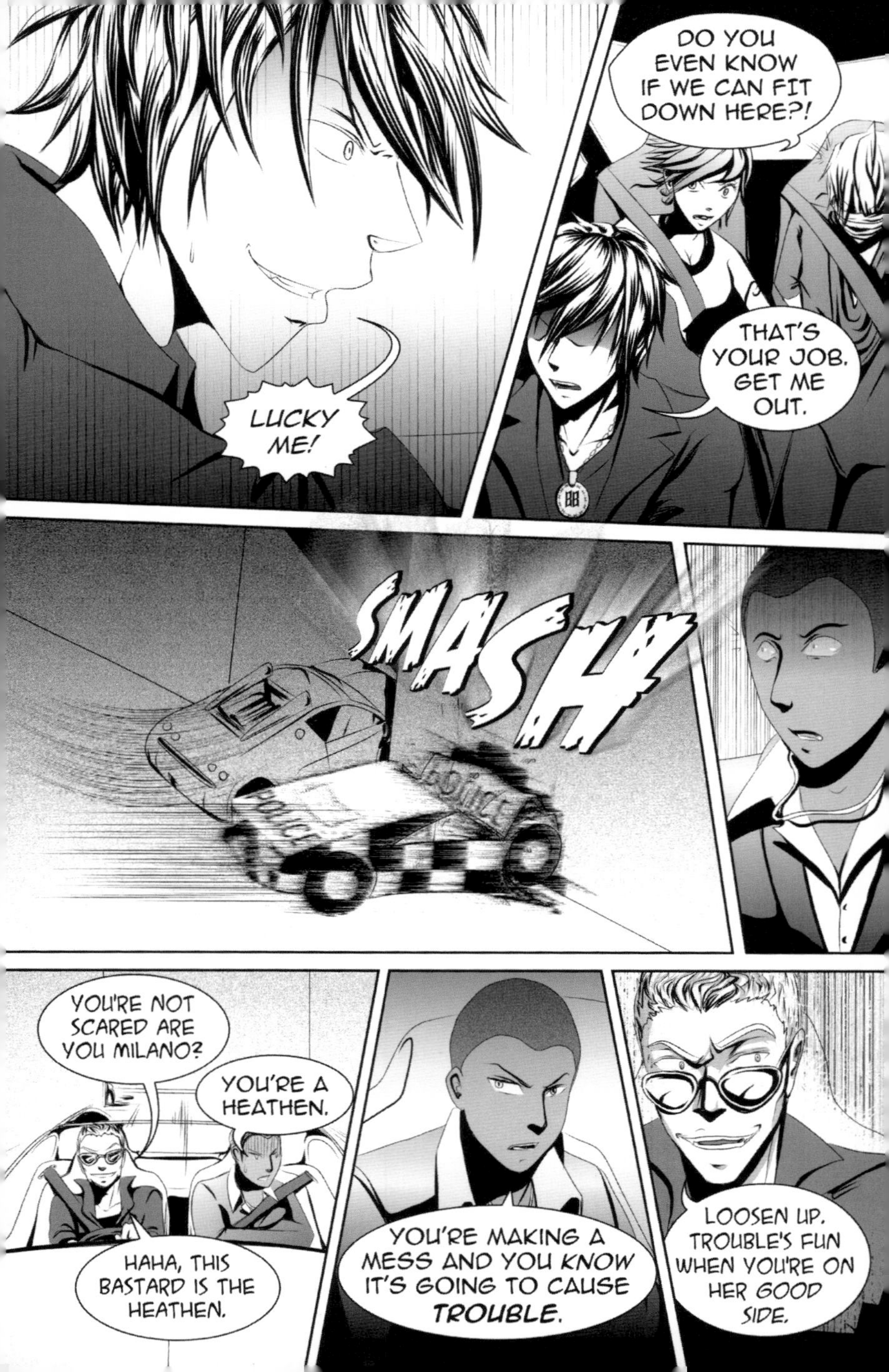

LUCKY ME!
DO YOU EVEN KNOW IF WE CAN FIT DOWN HERE?!
THAT'S YOUR JOB. GET ME OUT.
SMASH

BAD NEWS...
IT'S A DEAD END!

YOUR MISTAKE.
WHAT ARE YOU DOING?
IS HE CRAZY?
YOU'LL KILL US!!
SORRY BABY, THIS IS GONNA HURT.

SLAM

I'M... I'M ALIVE!
THUD

GREAT. NOW DO YOUR DAMN JOB AND GET ME OUT OF HERE!!
YOU'RE SO RUDE!
I'D RATHER BE RUDE THAN DEAD!
THERE ARE ONLY TWO EXITS. THE WAY WE CAME, WHICH IS BLOCKED, OR A HARD RIGHT.
THERE ARE ELECTRONIC BOLLARDS, SO WE MIGHT BE TRAPPED.
HAVE MERCY ON ME TODAY...

YES!!
HAHA HAA!
IS THIS A JOKE?!
FREAKING BOLLARDS?!
CAUTION: BARRIER RISING
THANK YOU FOR YOUR PATIENCE!
I HATE THAT GUY.
SMYTHE, YOU HATE EVERYBODY.

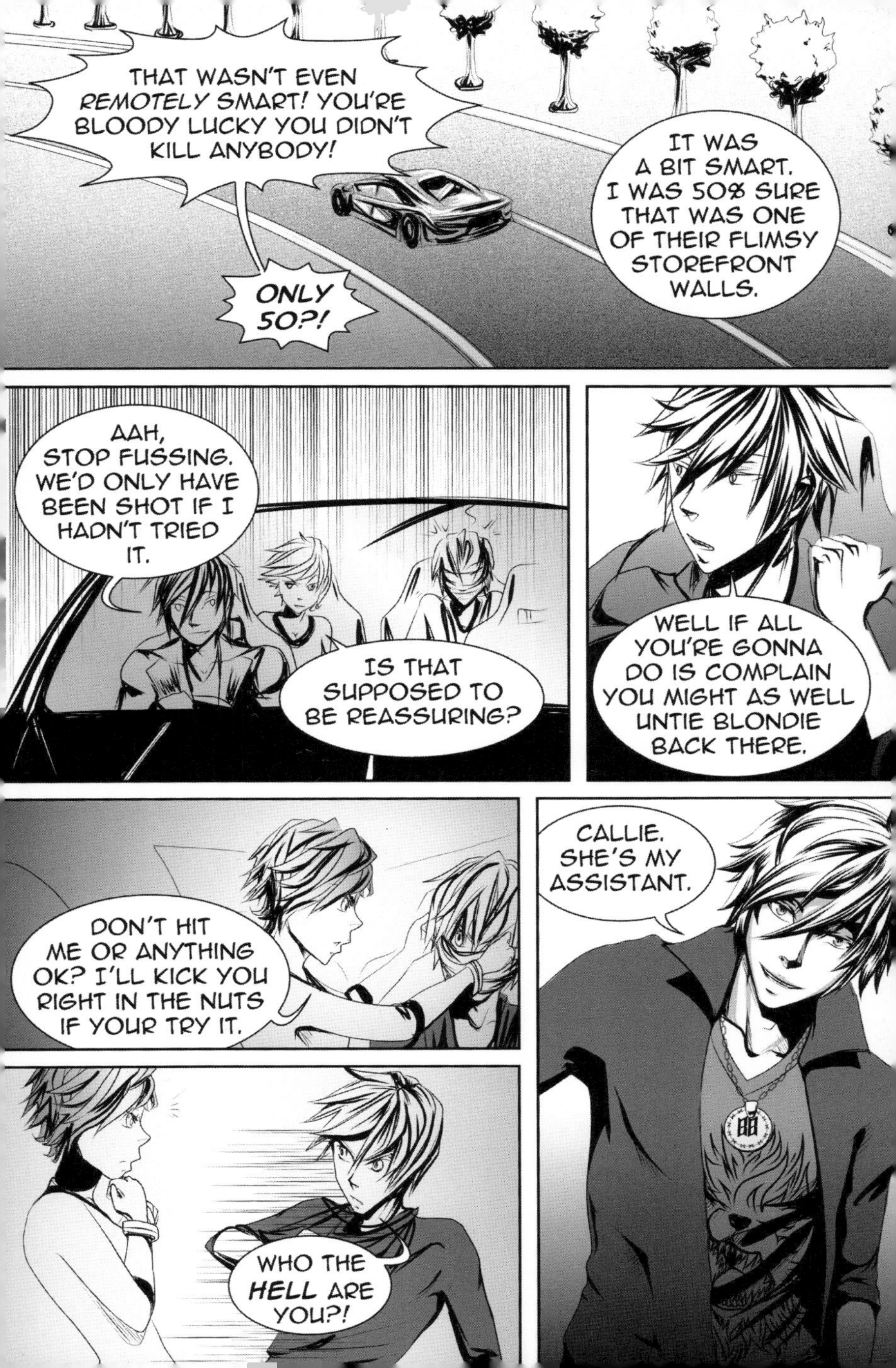

THAT WASN'T EVEN *REMOTELY* SMART! YOU'RE BLOODY LUCKY YOU DIDN'T KILL ANYBODY!

IT WAS A BIT SMART. I WAS 50% SURE THAT WAS ONE OF THEIR FLIMSY STOREFRONT WALLS.

ONLY 50?!

AAH, STOP FUSSING. WE'D ONLY HAVE BEEN SHOT IF I HADN'T TRIED IT.

IS THAT SUPPOSED TO BE REASSURING?

WELL IF ALL YOU'RE GONNA DO IS COMPLAIN YOU MIGHT AS WELL UNTIE BLONDIE BACK THERE.

KAI?!
IT'S BEEN A WHILE, HASN'T IT?
WHAT THE HELL?
STOP SHOUTING, I'M GETTING A HEADACHE.
YOU'RE GETTING A HEADACHE?
I'M THE ONE WHOSE HEAD IS BLEEDING!
PAT PAT
OH YEAH, SO IT IS. THAT WAS A BIT HARSH CALLIE...
I'M GONNA REITERATE: WHAT THE HELL?
WHY DID STRANGE MEN TRY TO TAKE YOU AWAY, WHY DID WE KIDNAP YOU, OR WHY ARE THERE PEOPLE TRYING TO KILL US?
ALL OF THE ABOVE.
DUNNO.
EH?

WE TOOK YOU BECAUSE THEY WERE GOING TO KILL YOU.
I HAVE MORE QUESTIONS...
CAN YOU AT LEAST WAIT 'TIL WE GET INSIDE?
WHAT ABOUT BELLA?
THEY WERE SAYING SHE ESCAPED AND HAD SOME KINDA PLAN, IS THAT TRUE?
I DON'T KNOW WHAT YOU'RE TALKING ABOUT.
OUR MUTUAL FRIEND...
I DON'T HAVE A FRIEND BY THAT NAME.
NIGHTSHADE!? COME ON KAI, IT'S NO SECRET HOW MUCH YOU CARE ABOUT HER.

NIGHTSHADE IS NOT A FRIEND.

SOMETHING WRONG?
YEAH.
BELLA & KAI WERE INSEPARABLE. SHE TRIED TO KILL HIM AND HE STILL FORGAVE HER.
MAYBE HE SAW SENSE?
OR MAYBE HE'S HIDING SOMETHING.

CHARACTER PROFILE

FULL NAME:
ANTONIO BALESTERO MASOMILIO
KNOWN AS: MASOMILIO
AGE: 45
HEIGHT: 6FT 7IN

MASOMILIO IS MOST PROMINENTLY KNOWN AS MAYOR AND CHIEF OFFICIAL OF THE CITY OF ASPEN. HE HAS BEEN IN OFFICE FOR 20 YEARS, WITH VERY LITTLE CHANCE FOR OPPOSITION, HAVING FIRST BEEN ELECTED AT THE AGE OF 25. HE IS A HIGHLY POPULAR FIGURE CREDITED FOR HIS POLITICAL, FINANCIAL AND SOCIAL INFLUENCE, WITH A CELEBRITY FOLLOWING (ESPECIALLY IN WOMEN'S MAGAZINES). HE ACTIVELY SEEKS OUT THE WORLD'S BEST TALENT FOR HIS PROJECTS AND PAYS HIGH SALARIES WITH INCREDIBLE BENEFITS IN ORDER TO KEEP THEM CLOSE AT HAND. HE HAS UNIQUELY SHARP, PALE BLUE EYES WHICH ARE QUITE CAPTIVATING, WITH AN ODD BRIGHTNESS TO THEM THAT MAKES PEOPLE WANT HIS ATTENTION AND APPRECIATION. HE ALSO HAS A KEEN EYE FOR FASHION, SPORTING DESIGNER SUITS MOST OF THE TIME. HIS CHARISMA IS INFECTIOUS AND MAKES PEOPLE FEEL IMPORTANT JUST BY BEING AROUND HIM, AND VERY FEW DARE ARGUE WITH HIM DUE TO THIS STAGGERING CONFIDENCE AND COMMAND OF THE ENGLISH LANGUAGE.

BEFORE HIS POLITICAL CAREER BEGAN HE WAS ALREADY A BIG NAME IN LOCAL INDUSTRY, HAVING MADE A FORTUNE BUYING AND SELLING PROPERTY AND LATER INVESTING IN TECHNOLOGY. MASOMILIO OWNS LARGE PORTIONS OF LAND WITHIN THE CITY ITSELF AND SEVERAL LARGE CORPORATIONS. HIS WEALTH IS IN EXCESS OF £2.5 BILLION. THE COMBINATION OF DECADES OF INDEPENDENT GROWTH, SECTARIAN DEVELOPMENT AND THE PROMINENCE OF AN INDIVIDUAL FIGUREHEAD HAVE RESULTED IN AN EXCESS OF POWER FAR BEYOND THE NORM FOR AN INDIVIDUAL IN MASOMILIO'S POSITION. THUS, HE IS THE MOST POWERFUL INDIVIDUAL IN THE STORY OF NIGHTSHADE, AND A HUGE POLITICAL FIGURE.

CHAPTER 2: MURDER'S MISTRESS

HM PRISON ASPEN,
A YEAR AGO...

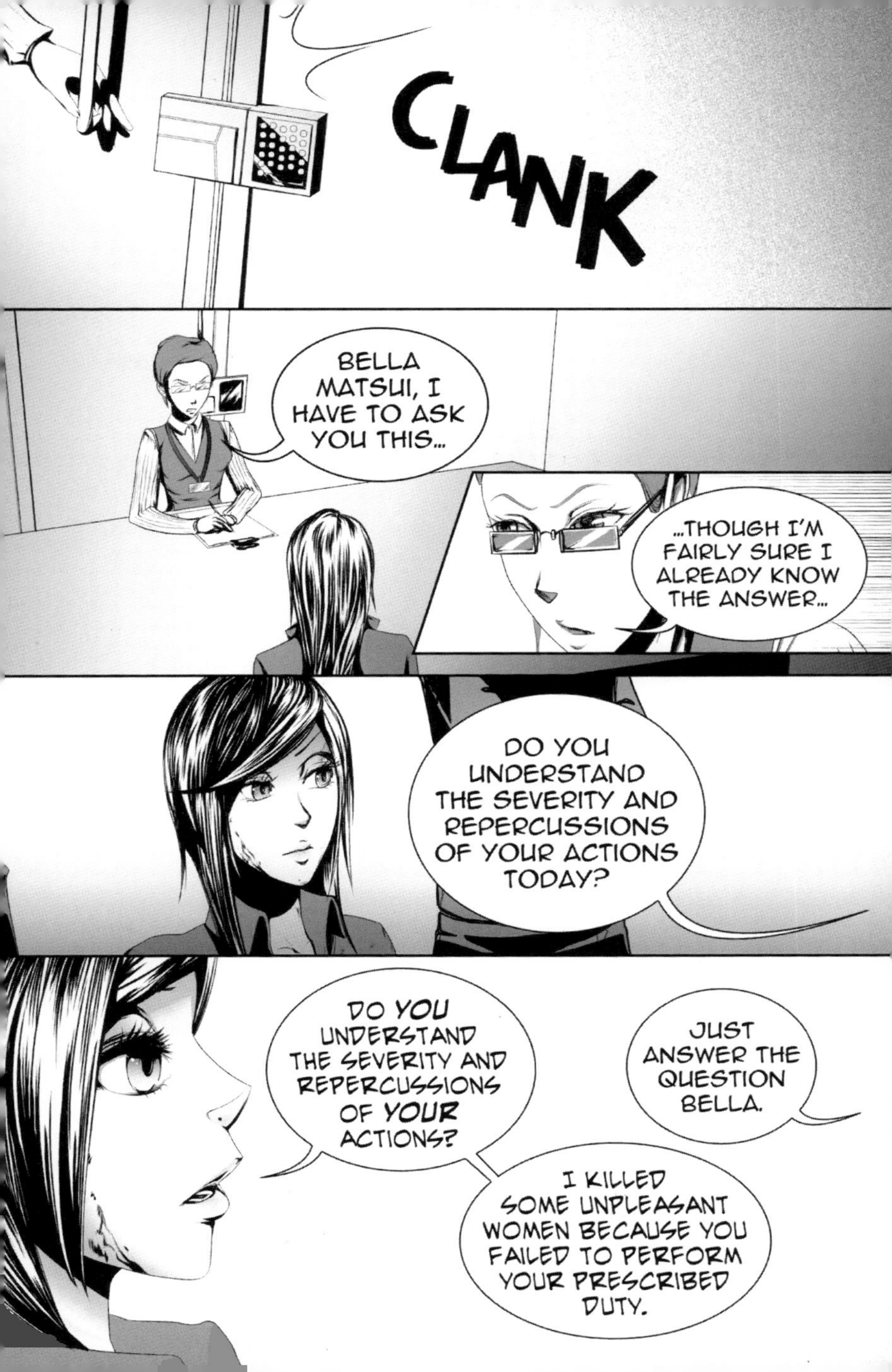
CLANK
BELLA MATSUI, I HAVE TO ASK YOU THIS...
...THOUGH I'M FAIRLY SURE I ALREADY KNOW THE ANSWER...
DO YOU UNDERSTAND THE SEVERITY AND REPERCUSSIONS OF YOUR ACTIONS TODAY?
DO *YOU* UNDERSTAND THE SEVERITY AND REPERCUSSIONS OF *YOUR* ACTIONS?
JUST ANSWER THE QUESTION BELLA.
I KILLED SOME UNPLEASANT WOMEN BECAUSE YOU FAILED TO PERFORM YOUR PRESCRIBED DUTY.

I DO MY JOB BELLA, AND I DO IT WELL.
YOU ISOLATED & KILLED 5 PEOPLE WITHIN THE SPACE OF AN HOUR.
OH I SEE, I HADN'T REALISED IT WAS YOUR JOB TO GET ME KILLED.
AND I SUPPOSE I'VE PLAYED RIGHT INTO YOUR HANDS, YES? IF YOU CAN'T KILL ME, DEMONIZATION WILL DO.
YOU ARE IN PRISON FOR MURDER. IF YOU WERE KILLED BY ANOTHER INMATE IT WOULD SIMPLY BE AN UNFORTUNATE CONSEQUENCE OF YOUR OWN MISDEMEANOUR.
I PREFER TO THINK OF IT AS THE UNFORTUNATE CONS-EQUENCE OF YOUR SLACK JAW.
I WOULDN'T BE SO HAPPY IF I WERE YOU. SURE, I'M GOING DOWN AS A SERIAL KILLER, BUT YOUR ESTEEMED CAREER IS OVER WHEN THIS GETS OUT.
AND HOW EXACTLY WILL THAT HAPPEN?

THIS PAIR ARE LIKELY UNDER YOUR THUMB, BUT THE ROOM IS MONITORED BY VIDEO SURVEILLANCE AND THE MANDATORY SECURITY BEHIND THAT WINDOW.
NOT EVERYONE WILL SHARE YOUR PERSONAL BRAND OF JUSTICE.
I AM NOT FOOLISH ENOUGH TO ENTER A ROOM WITH YOU ALONE....
...HOWEVER...
...WHAT WE SAY IN HERE WILL NOT GET PAST THESE FOUR WALLS.

SMACK

COME ON...
COME ON!!
WHY ISN'T IT WORKING?!
DID YOU THINK THIS WAS ALL A COINCIDENCE?

YOU'RE PROVING ME RIGHT ABOUT YOU!
IS THAT WHAT YOU WANT? BECAUSE YOU DON'T HAVE TO. YOU CAN STILL-
STAY IN THIS ENDLESS VOID WITH A PSYCHIATRIST WHO WANTS TO KILL ME?
RIP
TO BE HONEST, I'M SURPRISED SOMEONE IN YOUR LINE OF WORK WOULD BE FOOLISH ENOUGH TO ENGAGE WITH SOMEONE LIKE ME.
YOU REALLY SHOULD HAVE KNOWN BETTER.

CREAK

I'M NOT QUITE SURE WHETHER TO THANK OR PUNISH YOU FOR THE PROVOCATION, BUT I'M OPPOSED TO ACTING ON IMPULSE THESE DAYS.

THE THING IS DOCTOR, YOU THOUGHT YOU KNEW ME.
BUT EVEN NOW, PETRIFIED, SHAKING AND BEARING THE WEIGHT OF YOUR ENTIRE BODY ON THAT FRAGILE THROAT...

YOU STILL CAN'T IMAGINE THE THE PAIN I'VE KNOWN.
AND IF YOU CAN'T DO THAT THEN YOU'LL NEVER BE ABLE TO WRAP YOUR HEAD AROUND THE HORRORS I AM CAPABLE OF.
FOR EXAMPLE, I KNOW THAT THERE'S A RETINA SCANNER ON THE WAY OUT OF HERE.
WHAT I DON'T KNOW IS WHETHER OR NOT TO KILL YOU BEFORE TAKING WHAT I NEED...
SOMETIMES I THINK I MUST HAVE SEEN THE CONTENTS OF SO MANY SKULLS THAT I'VE LOST THE GAG REFLEX...
...BUT I DIGRESS.

THIS MAY BE DIFFICULT FOR YOU TO BELIEVE, BUT THERE WAS A TIME WHEN I SINCERELY WANTED TO CHANGE.
I LET YOU WITNESS THE GRUESOME REALITY OF MY PSYCHE SO YOU COULD HELP ME HEAL IT...
...BUT YOU TOOK THAT CONFIDENCE AND USED IT AGAINST ME, LETTING THE RESIDENT **SABRES** IN ON MY IDENTITY.
IN CASE YOU DIDN'T KNOW, GANGSTERS ***DON'T*** LIKE IT WHEN YOU KILL THEIR BOSS.

THEY CUT ME OPEN.
BUT YOU KNOW THAT, DON'T YOU? IT WAS DOCTOR'S ORDERS AFTER ALL.
I'LL BE HONEST, WHEN I WOKE UP IN THE INFIRMARY WITH A STOMACH FULL OF SUTURES I THOUGHT I'D DIED AND GONE TO HELL.
I WISHED I HAD.
BUT THEN I REALIZED SOMETHING PRETTY FUNNY.

IT WAS NEVER MY IDEA TO BE WELL BEHAVED. I'M GOOD AT SURVIVING, BUT WHEN I TRY TO LIVE BY THE MORAL STANDARDS OF OTHER PEOPLE I FIND MYSELF SUFFERING.
I AM CAPABLE OF SO MUCH MORE AS LONG AS I REFUSE TO CONTINUE DYING FOR YOU PEOPLE.
...WHICH BRINGS ME ONTO MY NEXT POINT; DR CASEY...
MOST PEOPLE KNOW VERY LITTLE ABOUT DOWNTOWN. BUT THIS WOMAN WHO LEAKED THE IDENTITY OF A DOWNTOWN CRIMINAL TO MEMBERS OF A DOWNTOWN GANG SURE KNOWS A LOT ABOUT DOWNTOWN!

SO... HOW DO YOU KNOW SO MUCH?
I WORK IN A PRISON! I TALK TO THESE PEOPLE!
NOT GOOD ENOUGH.
WHAT'S REALLY GOING ON? WHAT'S STANDING IN THE GAP BETWEEN THESE TWO SOCIETIES THAT KEEPS EACH BLIND TO THE OTHER?
I...I DON'T KNOW!
LIAR!
THIS DID NOT COME FROM NOWHERE!

IT WAS YOUR DOING BASED ON YOUR KNOWLEDGE!
YOU KNOW ABOUT SABRE, RAVEN, SKYLARK, NIGHTSHADE AND I'D BET MY BLOODY CARCASS, A WHOLE LOT MORE!
SO THINK ABOUT THIS...
...AND I'D SUGGEST YOU THINK VERY CAREFULLY, BECAUSE IT'S THE LAST TIME I'LL ASK...
IS THERE SOMETHING MORE I MIGHT LIKE TO KNOW?
DOWNTOWN IS A GHETTO. IT'S RUN BY GANGS AND THERE'S A STRONG PREVALENCE OF WEAPONS AND DRUGS.

YOU KNOW DAMN WELL THAT'S NOT WHAT I ASKED FOR.
I HAVE NOTHING ELSE TO SAY.
IN THAT CASE...
MAKING SURE I DON'T GET BLOOD ON YOUR CLOTHES.
WHAT ARE YOU DOING?!
WAIT, WAIT!
THIS GOD-FORSAKEN PLACE IS FULL OF SHAMELESS CRIMINALS GUILTY OF DISGUSTING CRIMES.
I WAS ALLOWED TO KNOW THE TRUTH!
ALL I DO IS MAINTAIN THE CIRCULATION OF INFORMATION!
AND THE COURTS BARELY KNEW THE HALF OF IT!
SOMEBODY HAD TO REGULATE THE PRISON POPULATION AND GIVE THOSE THUGS WHAT THEY REALLY DESERVED!

THEY COULD NEVER INTEGRATE WITH SOCIETY. THEY WERE VIOLENT TO THE CORE. IT WAS BETTER THAT THEY-
DIE?
YOU IDIOT. YOUR IDEAOLOGY IS JUST AS TWISTED AS THE ONES YOU LOVE TO HATE AND YOU'RE TOTALLY BLIND TO IT.
THE PEOPLE OF UPTOWN ARE NO BETTER THAN THOSE DOWNTOWN, THEY JUST HAVEN'T HAD THE PLEASURE OF FIGHTING FOR THEIR LIVES YET!
AND WHO KNOWS? PERHAPS WHEN IT'S BROUGHT TO THE BOIL THEY ALL LOOK JUST AS BLISTERED AND DEFORMED!

WHILE YOU VINDICATE YOURSELF WITH EXCUSES, I SEE MY ACTIONS IN THEIR PURE, UNADULTERATED REALITY!
I'LL ADMIT THAT I'M COLD AND CALLOUS TO THE BONE...
THERE'S NOTHING GRATIFYING OR JUSTIFIABLE ABOUT ANY OF THIS!
...AND I HAVE NO QUALMS ABOUT ACCEPTING RESPOSIBILITY FOR THAT.
IT'S FUNCTIONAL. NOTHING MORE, NOTHING LESS.
BUT YOU ALL HELPED FORM ME, AND I'LL BE DAMNED IF YOU DON'T DIE KNOWING IT.

THE BEST USE OF AN OLD, BROKEN MACHINE IS TO STRIP IT APART FOR PIECES OF SCRAP.
WE'LL HAVE TO SEE WHETHER THERE'S ANYTHING IN THIS SYSTEM WORTH SALVAGING.
BUT FIRST...
WE DETHRONE THE KING.

YOU COULD HAVE BEEN A BIT MORE GENTLE!
TYING HIM UP WAS *YOUR* IDEA!
CALLIE'S NEVER GENTLE.
WE'D ALL BE DEAD IF I LET HIM HAVE A STROP IN THE CAR!
WHAT DID YOU EXPECT!?
I *EXPECTED* YOU TO BE AN UNGRATEFUL BRAT, BUT I'D *HOPED* YOU'D APPRECIATE NOT BEING DEAD.
I'M NOT CONVICED BEING HERE IS ANY BETTER.
GO HOME IF YOU LIKE. I WON'T STOP YOU.
FWUMP

DID HE JUST SIT ON-
YEP.
ARE YOU READY TO **DIE** SUCKER?!
AAAAAAAH!
LEO!

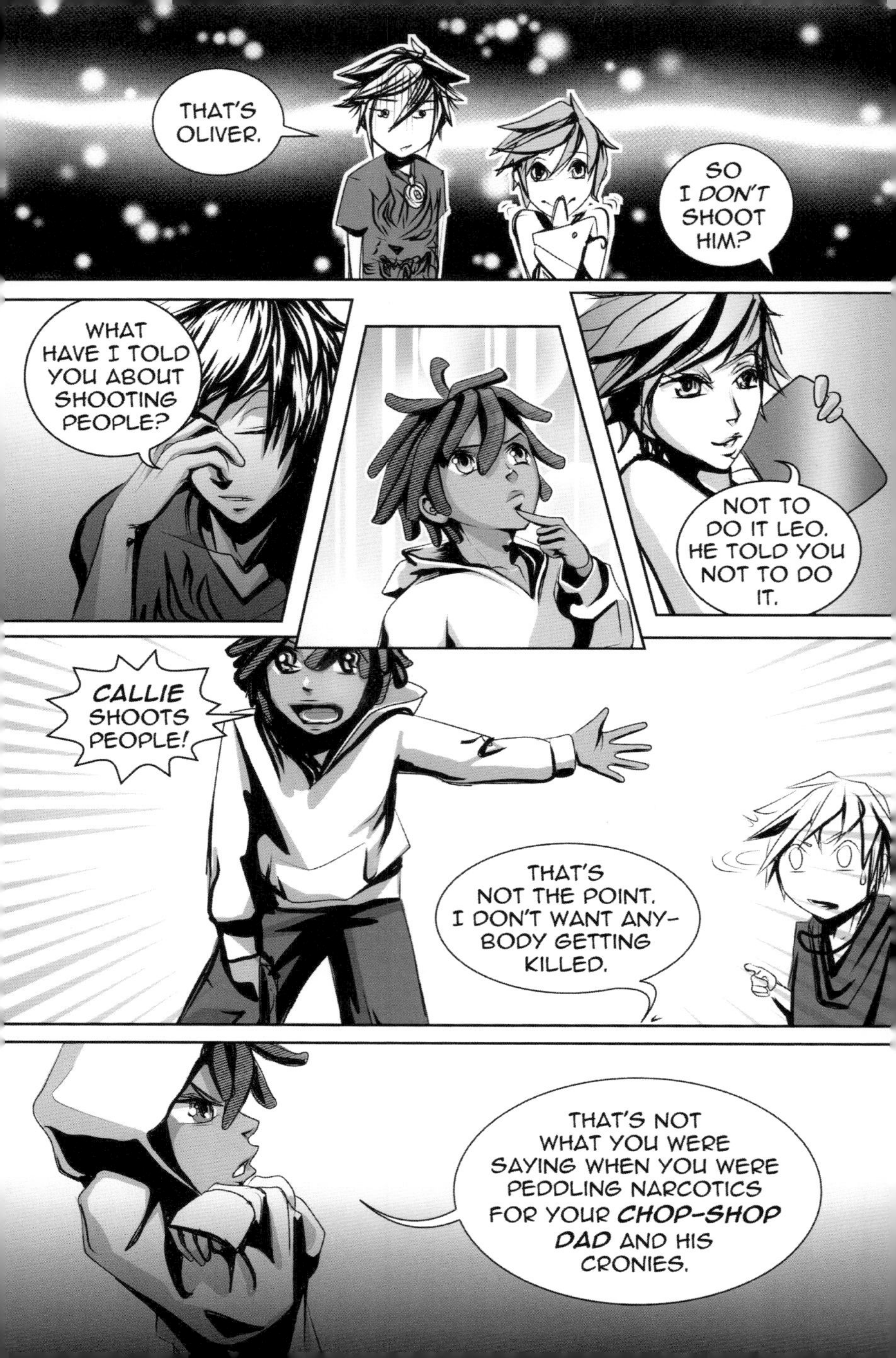

THAT'S OLIVER.

SO I *DON'T* SHOOT HIM?

WHAT HAVE I TOLD YOU ABOUT SHOOTING PEOPLE?

NOT TO DO IT LEO. HE TOLD YOU NOT TO DO IT.

CALLIE SHOOTS PEOPLE!

THAT'S NOT THE POINT. I DON'T WANT ANY-BODY GETTING KILLED.

YOU WANNA SAY THAT TO MY FACE LITTLE GUY?
WHO? ME? I WAS JUST TALKING TO MY NEW FRIEND HERE! HEHEH...
THAT SYMBOL ...
YOU'RE A RAVEN MEMBER?

EX-RAVEN. THE IDIOT FOLLOWED ME.

WELL, IT BEATS BEING A GANGSTER!
NO...
YOU WERE SAFER THERE.

ANYWAY, THE NAME'S LEO, IT'S NICE TO MEET YOU!

DON'T BE FOOLED, HIS REAL NAME IS LEE. HE JUST THINKS "LEO" SOUNDS COOLER.

IT'S NOTHING WEIRD! MY NAME'S LEE OKORO! SEE? LEE-O!

PLEASE CALL ME LEO, THESE GUYS ARE BRUTAL! I NEED YOU TO BE MY BRO, MAN!
UM, OK.

SO WHAT'S GOING ON EXACTLY?
WE'RE STANDING UP FOR JUSTICE!
SAYING NO TO NIGHTSHADE'S TYRANNY-
THERE ARE LOTS OF PEOPLE TRYING TO KILL US, AND WE'RE DOING OUR BEST NOT TO DIE.
YOU SURE DON'T SUGAR-COAT ANYTHING...
ER, WHO IS TRYING TO KILL US?
NIGHT-SHADE!!
TU CASSE LES ORIELLES.
SHUT UP LEE!
IT'S LEO!
YOU DON'T KNOW WHAT YOU'RE TALKING ABOUT. ALL YOU'RE DOING IS ADDING FUEL TO THE FIRE.
ADDING WHAT TO THE WHAT?

HOW ABOUT YOU MAKE UP FOR THOSE RUDE THINGS YOU SAID TO KAI WITH A NICE CUP OF TEA?
MAKE TEA? WHO DO YOU THINK I AM, YOUR LACKEY?!

WE'RE BEING PURSUED BY THREE DISTINCT GROUPS. SABRE AND RAVEN ARE TWO OF THOSE GROUPS.
SABRE'S MEN ARE ORGANISED AND HAVE GOOD CONNECTIONS BUT THEY ARE FEW IN NUMBER. RAVEN'S MEN ARE FAR LESS COMPOSED BUT *VERY* AGGRESSIVE.

I UNDERSTAND YOU'VE MET SOME OF THESE PEOPLE BEFORE, BUT IT CANNOT BE STRESSED ENOUGH HOW DANGEROUS THEY ARE.

YOU MENTIONED RAVEN AND SABRE BUT NOT SKYLARK... IS THAT THE THIRD GROUP?

NO, SKYLARK ISN'T PURSUING US.
THOSE MEN THAT TRIED TO KILL YOU ARE THE THIRD GROUP, BUT WE DON'T KNOW WHO THEY ARE.
THINKING ABOUT KAI? TREAD CARE- FULLY.
I DON'T KNOW WHAT HAPPENED, BUT NIGHTSHADE IS NOBODY'S FRIEND, *ESPECIALLY* NOT KAI'S.
WHATEVER SHE DID TO HIM, LEAVE IT ALONE. HE ISN'T STABLE.
...HE FEELS RESPONSIBLE FOR US, ESPECIALLY LEO, WHO LOOKS UP TO HIM.
AND THEN THERE'S THE MATTER OF HIS ROOTS.

HIS ROOTS?

KAI'S MOTHER DIED WHEN HE WAS 7, SO HE WAS RAISED BY HIS FATHER, KUGO.

...BUT KUGO WAS RAVEN'S ENFORCER; AN UNSTOPPABLE MONSTER WHOSE SOLE PURPOSE WAS TO PUNISH TRAITORS.

HIS SPECIALITY IS TO DISMEMBER TRAITORS WITH A SAW WHILE THEY'RE STILL BREATHING!

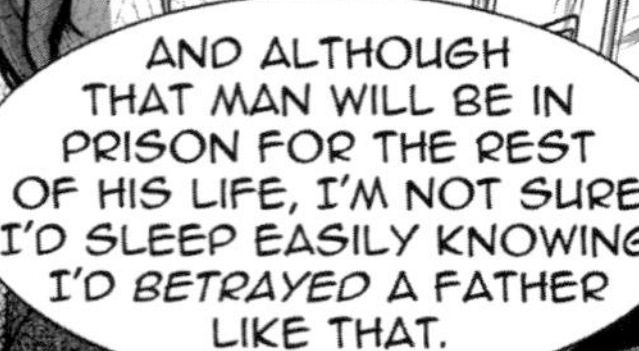

AND ALTHOUGH THAT MAN WILL BE IN PRISON FOR THE REST OF HIS LIFE, I'M NOT SURE I'D SLEEP EASILY KNOWING I'D *BETRAYED* A FATHER LIKE THAT.

SO DO YOU THINK YOU CAN AVOID MENTIONING THESE THINGS AROUND KAI?

I GUESS SO.

THANK YOU!

WHAT ABOUT YOU, CALLIE? HOW DO YOU FIT INTO ALL OF THIS?
ME? WELL I WAS BORN IN PARIS, CAME OVER HERE FOR WORK AND... WHAT CAN I SAY? I MET KAI!
KAI IS YOUR BOSS?
OUI! I'M HIS ASSISTANT, AND HIS NAVIGATOR, BUT I'M GOOD WITH ALL SORTS OF DEVICES SO I GATHER INFORMATION TO KEEP US SAFE!
SHE'S VERY INTELLIGENT.
SHE'S VERY *MEAN!* WHERE'S THE TEA?
WE'RE ALL OUT OF TEA.
WE'RE OUT OF TEA?!
AIN'T THAT TRAGIC!
WE'LL DO SOME SHOPPING TOMORROW.

OLI!
YOU DRINK CIDER?
MM?
UM...
I'LL HAVE ONE.

YOU'RE UNDERAGE.
RAVEN LET ME DRINK!
YEAH, AND ISN'T HE A BRILLIANT ROLE MODEL...

MOM DOESN'T LIKE US DRINKING. SHE SAYS IT MAKES DAD UNCOOPERATIVE.
WELL, IT'S ALL I'VE GOT. WE CAN GET SOMETHING ELSE TOMORROW.

THIS MIGHT BE AN ODD QUESTION, BUT YOU HAVEN'T HAD ANY CONTACT WITH RAVEN, HAVE YOU?
ME?! NOT LIKELY! WHY?

A FEW MONTHS AGO HE STARTED HUNTING US WITH A VENGEANCE BUT I DON'T KNOW WHY.

YOU LEFT, LEO LEFT, HE'D COME AFTER YOU FOR THAT RIGHT?
HE DID, BUT THIS IS DIFFERENT. I KNOW RAVEN, THIS SUDDEN CHANGE IS EXTREME, EVEN FOR HIM...

WHO ARE HIS CLOSEST CONTACTS?
I CAN TAP INTO SMS COM-MUNICATIONS BETWEEN THE GANG MEMBERS. SEE IF IT SHEDS ANY LIGHT ON THE MATTER.

THE CLOSEST WOULD HAVE TO BE ARABELLE CHALK. THEY'RE IN CONSTANT CONTACT.

ARABELLE? IS THAT THE GIRL THAT THE BROTHER-HOOD SPLIT UP OVER?
YES.
WHO IS SHE TO HIM?
RAVEN'S GIRLFRIEND.

HOW CAN ***RAVEN*** HAVE A GIRLFRIEND? HE'S ALWAYS WITH A DIFFERENT WOMAN!!

ER... "GIRLFRIEND" PROBABLY ISN'T THE RIGHT WORD. THEY'RE IN TOUCH SO HE CAN SEE HIS SON FROM TIME TO TIME.

SAMMY!

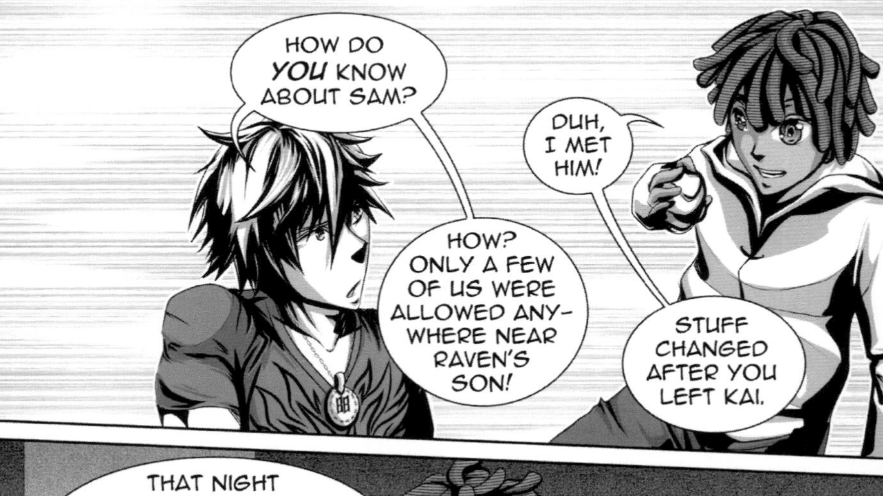

HOW DO ***YOU*** KNOW ABOUT SAM?
DUH, I MET HIM!
HOW? ONLY A FEW OF US WERE ALLOWED ANY-WHERE NEAR RAVEN'S SON!
STUFF CHANGED AFTER YOU LEFT KAI.

THAT NIGHT YOU TURNED TRAITOR RAVEN GOT JUMPED BY SKYLARK'S GUYS AND THEY SHOT HIM A BUNCH OF TIMES.
IT WAS A CLOSE CALL, BUT HE WAS BROUGHT BACK FROM THE BRINK OF DEATH BY THE SUPER-DOCTOR! AFTER THAT, RAVEN & ARABELLE GOT CLOSER AND THAT'S WHEN I MET SAM.

NOTHING LIKE A NEAR-DEATH EXPERIENCE TO WIN A WOMAN'S HEART...
HE STAYED DOWNTOWN? DO YOU KNOW WHAT SKYLARK WOULD DO TO RAVEN'S SON?! PEOPLE DIED PROTECTING THAT KID!

I DUNNO MAN. RAVEN REALLY LOVES HIS KID.

ALRIGHT, I'LL HAVE A LOOK THROUGH ARABELLE'S PHONE. IF I GET NOTHING, WHO ELSE CAN I TRY?
THE EMPRESS; HER FULL NAME IS ROXANNA SHARPE. OR HIS DOCTOR; JON WALKER. THEY'RE THE ONLY PEOPLE HE REALLY TRUSTS.

ON IT.

HEY CALLIE, HOW DO YOU HACK INTO PHONES?

SO WHAT DO YOU THINK?
YOU'RE UNSTABLE, LEO'S INSANE AND CALLIE SEEMS REALLY SMART, FORGIVE ME IF I DON'T FEEL COMPLETELY SAFE.
TRUE, BUT THEY'RE NICE, SO THERE'S NOTHING TO WORRY ABOUT.
NICE?! CALLIE SMACKED MY HEAD AGAINST A CAR DOOR 'TIL IT BLED!

SHE DOESN'T KILL PEOPLE. I LIKE THAT IN A WOMAN.
REALLY? YOU COULDA' FOOLED ME!

WELL YOU COULD AT LEAST GET TO KNOW HER BEFORE YOU START LEERING.
EH?! THERE WAS NO LEERING! WHAT ARE YOU, HER DAD?!

NOT SURE HOW YOU CAN CRITICISE GIVEN *YOUR* DATING HISTORY...
YOU DON'T KNOW MY DATING HISTORY.
EVERYONE KNOWS *YOUR* DATING HISTORY.

AT LEAST *MINE'S* NOT A LAPTOP..

SHADE

NIGHTSHADE
THIS
#1
01.04.18

CHARACTER PROFILE

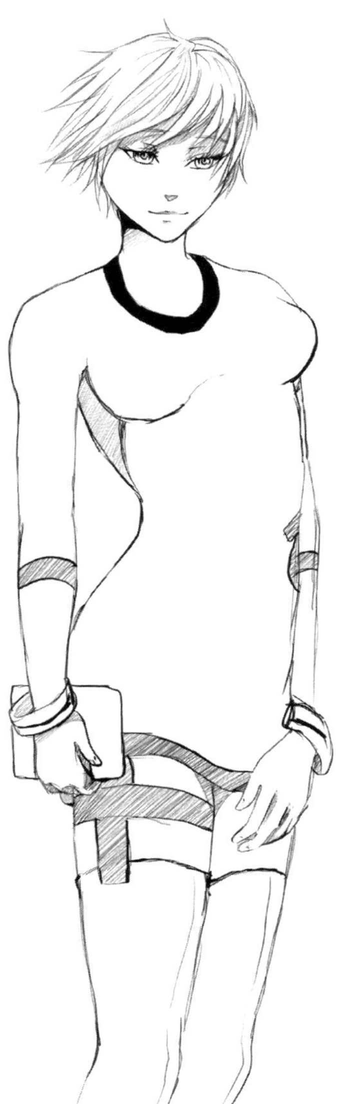

FULL NAME: CALLIE VIENNA
KNOWN AS: CALLIE
AGE: 24
HEIGHT: 5FT 9IN

BORN TO WEALTHY PARENTS AND RAISED IN VERSAILLES, FRANCE; CALLIE HAS ALWAYS KNOWN A LIFE OF LUXURY. SHE DID WELL IN EDUCATION AND WENT ON TO STUDY AT ONE OF FRANCE'S MOST PRESTIGIOUS INSTITUTIONS. ALTHOUGH HER HIGHER EDUCATION FOCUSED ON ENGINEERING, SHE MANAGED TO ATTAIN A HIGH STANDARD OF PROFICIENCY IN LANGUAGES, SCIENCES AND EVEN MILITARY LEARNING. SHE MOVED TO THE UK IN 2017 AFTER BEING DISCOVERED BY A WEALTHY BUSINESSMAN. SHORTLY AFTER BEGINNING HER CAREER, HOWEVER, SHE CAME TO WORK FOR KAI INSTEAD, TRAVELLING WITH HIM UNDER DUBIOUS AND ILLEGAL CIRCUMSTANCES. NONTHELESS, SHE DOES WELL UNDER PRESSURE AND HAS KEPT THEM ALIVE MANY TIMES THANKS TO HER SKILLS.

THOUGH NONE OF THEM FULLY UNDERSTAND HER REASONS FOR JOINING THEM, IT IS CLEAR THAT SHE IS COMPASSIONATE FOR THEIR SITUATION AND DOES HER BEST TO PROTECT THE TEAM.

CHARACTER PROFILE

FULL NAME: LEE OKORO
KNOWN AS: LEO
AGE: 16
HEIGHT: 5FT 4IN
LEO HAS A VIBRANT PERSONALITY AND EXUDES OVERWHELMING POSITIVITY IN THE FACE OF ANY SITUATION. HE HAS A GREAT DEAL OF RESPECT FOR KAI DUE TO HIS STRONG SENSE OF MORALITY AND BRAVERY IN UPHOLDING IT.
LEO JOINED RAVEN AT THE AGE OF 14, ON THE SAME DAY HIS OLDER BROTHER DIO JOINED SKYLARK. THIS WAS DUE TO A MISUNDERSTANDING BETWEEN THE TWO, WHO HAD RECENTLY LOST THEIR ONLY PARENT, AND NEEDED TO FIND A WAY OF SURVIVING ON THEIR OWN. TRAGICALLY, THE PRESSURES OF DEMONSTRATING LOYALTY TO THEIR NEWFOUND GANGS PARTED THE BROTHERS FOR A LITTLE OVER A YEAR, UNTIL THEY FOUND THEMSELVES FACING EACH OTHER DOWN. SCARED FOR HIS LIFE AND PRESSURED INTO SUBMISSION, LEO SHOT HIS BROTHER. THE MEMORY HAS HAUNTED HIM EVER SINCE, AND AFTER HEARING THE STIORIES OF KAI'S BETRAYAL OF THE GANG, HE DECIDED TO RUN AWAY AND FIND HIM. UNDERSTANDING THE PRESSURES OF LIFE DOWNTOWN, KAI TOOK PITY ON LEO, AND TOOK HIM IN, ENCOURAGING THE BOY TO KEEP LIVING, AND TRY TO BE THE BEST PERSON HE CAN.
LEO CHOSE TO CALL HIMSELF LEO (RATHER THAN LEE) AFTER RUNNING AWAY WITH KAI IN AN EFFORT TO PUT HIS PAST BEHIND HIM.

CHAPTER 3: BEHIND THE SMILE

Firing
Line

YOU'RE NERVOUS.
HOW DID YOU-
RELAX. IT'S NOT LIKE YOU'RE ON THE HOTSEAT.
I WORRY ABOUT BRINGING A POLITICIAN ONTO A SHOW LIKE OURS WITH ALL THAT'S BEEN GOING ON LATELY.
WELL FROM MY PERSPECTIVE, IT'S A CHANCE TO EXPLAIN WHAT'S GOING ON.
I CERTAINLY HOPE YOU'RE RIGHT, I VOTED FOR YOU!
WE GO LIVE IN 5...
Firing Line
...4... 3...
...2... 1...

GOOD EVENING!
WELCOME TO FIRING LINE, THE SHOW THAT GIVES YOU CHANCE TO ASK THOSE BURNING QUESTIONS...

THIS WEEK, WE HAVE A ***VERY*** SPECIAL GUEST!
MR. MASOMILIO, WHAT A PLEASURE TO HAVE YOU ON THE SHOW.

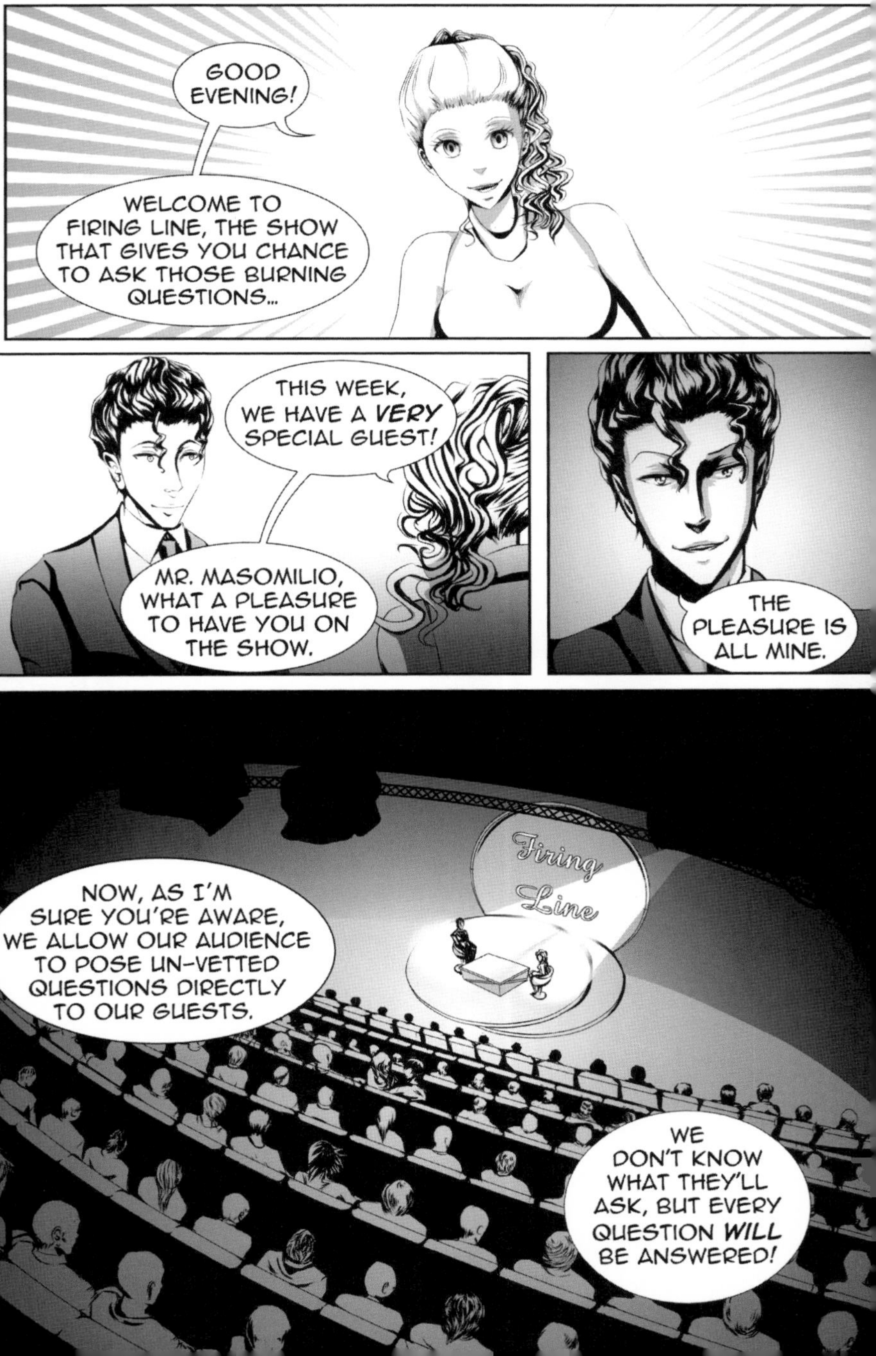

THE PLEASURE IS ALL MINE.

Firing Line
NOW, AS I'M SURE YOU'RE AWARE, WE ALLOW OUR AUDIENCE TO POSE UN-VETTED QUESTIONS DIRECTLY TO OUR GUESTS.
WE DON'T KNOW WHAT THEY'LL ASK, BUT EVERY QUESTION ***WILL*** BE ANSWERED!

I'D HATE TO SAY WE'RE GOING TO GRILL YOU, BUT IT COULD BE AN ENLIGHTENING EVENING!
MM, NO AMOUNT OF REVISION CAN PREPARE ME FOR THIS CAN IT?
THEY'RE GOING TO WANT DIRT ON YOU!
HAHA!
GO ON. YOU'D BETTER SET THEM LOOSE.

HOW DO YOU BALANCE BEING A POLITICIAN *AND* A BUSINESS MAN?
WHICH OF YOUR ACHIEVEMENTS MEANS THE MOST TO YOU?
HOW MUCH DID IT COST TO BUILD MAPLE BOULEVARD?
IT'S SIMPLE REALLY, POLITICS AND BUSINESS GO HAND IN HAND!
NO SINGLE ACCOMPLISHMENT CAN OUTWEIGH THE JOY OF KNOWING OUR CITY IS THE PINNACLE OF MODERN LIVING.
THE MAPLE BOULEVARD TOWER WAS APPROXIMATELY £400 MILLION TO CONSTRUCT.
WHAT'S THE SECRET TO YOUR SUCCESS?
MY, THIS DOESN'T SEEM SO BAD...
I WORK HARD, FIGHT FOR WHAT MATTERS AND INVEST IN THE FUTURE.
HAVE YOU EVER CHEATED ON YOUR WIFE?
...
MY WIFE AND BOYS ARE MY WORLD, I COULD NEVER HURT THEM LIKE THAT.

HELP KEEP OUR STREETS SAFE!
WHY WON'T YOU ACCEPT RESPONSIBILITY FOR THE DILAPIDATED AREAS AT THE EDGE OF THE CITY?
I HEARD PEOPLE STILL LIVE THERE.
FROM TIME TO TIME VAGRANTS SETTLE IN DERELICT AREAS, BUT THEY ARE SOON CLEARED OUT.
I'LL ADMIT THAT THOSE DUSTY OLD BUILDINGS TAKE UP LAND THAT COULD BE USED BETTER, BUT THERE'S NOTHING *I* CAN DO ABOUT IT.
YOU REALLY SHOULDN'T BELIEVE EVERYTHING YOU HEAR.
NO... YOU REALLY SHOULDN'T.

I'D LIKE TO ASK ABOUT THE HIGH SPEED CAR CHASE THAT BOMBED RIGHT DOWN MAPLE BOULEVARD!!
CAN YOU PHRASE THAT AS A QUESTION?
WHY DID IT HAPPEN? WHAT ARE YOU DOING ABOUT IT?
I DON'T KNOW WHY THOSE PEOPLE CHOSE TO PUT LIVES AT RISK BY DOING SOMETHING SO IRRESPONSIBLE.
FORTUNATELY, NOBODY WAS HURT, BUT SUCH AN INCIDENT WILL NOT BE PERMITTED TO HAPPEN AGAIN.
IS IT TRUE THERE WAS GUNFIRE?
GUNFIRE? NO, OF COURSE NOT! MAPLE BOULEVARD IS ESSENTIALLY MY FRONT DOOR!

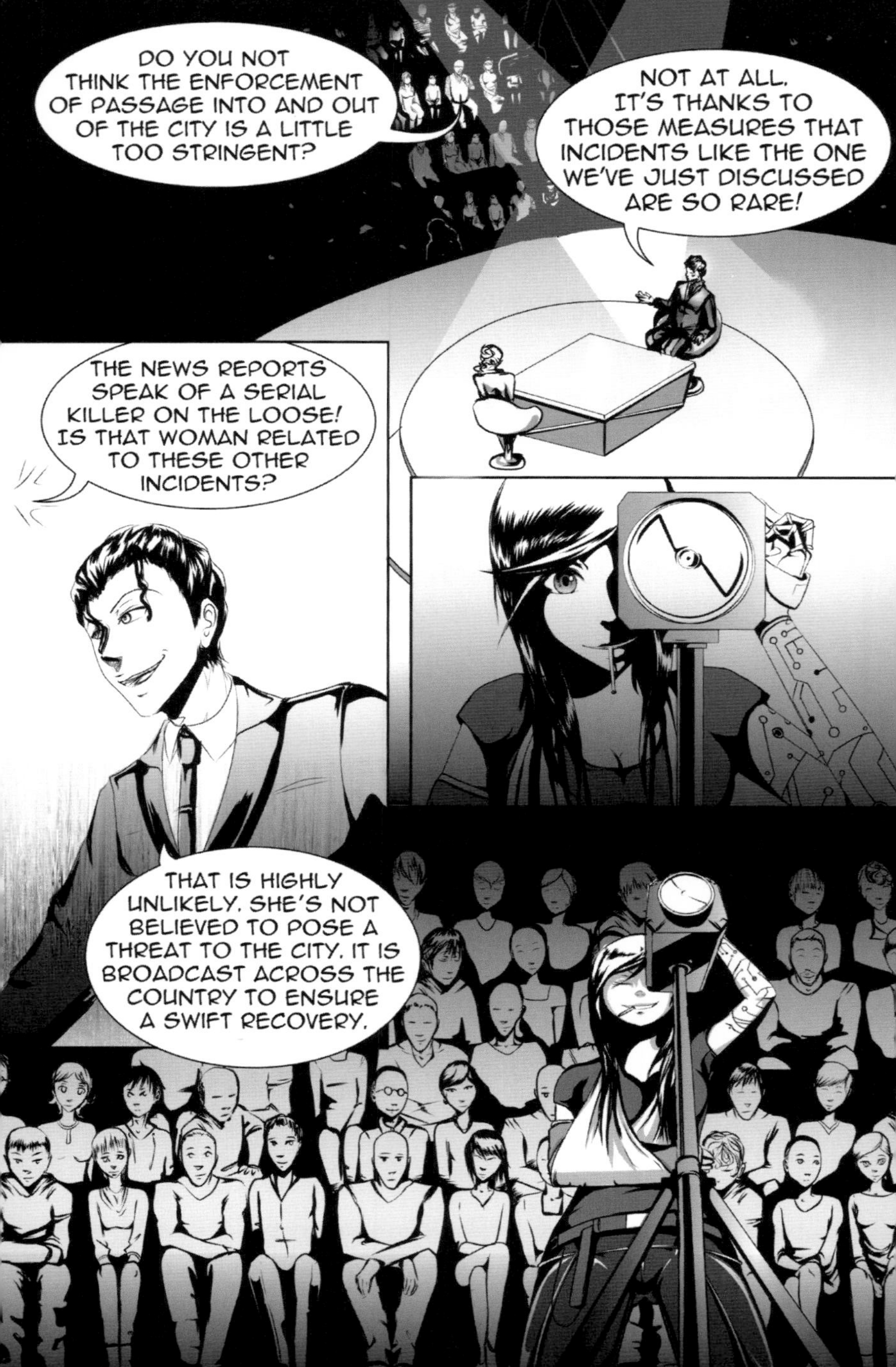
DO YOU NOT THINK THE ENFORCEMENT OF PASSAGE INTO AND OUT OF THE CITY IS A LITTLE TOO STRINGENT?
NOT AT ALL. IT'S THANKS TO THOSE MEASURES THAT INCIDENTS LIKE THE ONE WE'VE JUST DISCUSSED ARE SO RARE!
THE NEWS REPORTS SPEAK OF A SERIAL KILLER ON THE LOOSE! IS THAT WOMAN RELATED TO THESE OTHER INCIDENTS?
THAT IS HIGHLY UNLIKELY. SHE'S NOT BELIEVED TO POSE A THREAT TO THE CITY. IT IS BROADCAST ACROSS THE COUNTRY TO ENSURE A SWIFT RECOVERY.

YOU HANDLED THAT VERY WELL.
YOU WEREN'T KIDDING WHEN YOU SAID THEY'D GRILL ME!
THIS PAST WEEK HAS BEEN THE MOST EVENTFUL IN YEARS, BUT YOU HANDLED EVERYBODY'S QUESTIONS WITHOUT BREAKING A SWEAT. YOU REALLY ARE PERFECT FOR YOUR JOB.

YOU FLATTER ME, ELIZABETH.
IF THERE'S ANYTHING MORE I CAN DO FOR YOU GIVE ME A CALL.

HUCK!?
SMACK

SO SORRY SIR!
NOT TO WORRY!
CREW
KUHUHU...
...CANDY FROM A BABY.

AH.

WHY, YOU LITTLE...
!
GET OUT OF MY CITY.
ALL OF YOU.

WELL, HELLO GORGEOUS!

!?!

NOW NOW. NO NEED TO USE THAT SORT OF LANGUAGE...
YES... YES, I KNOW...

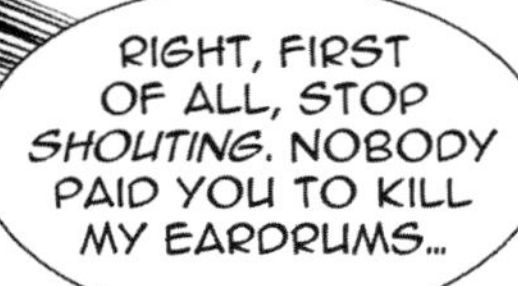
RIGHT, FIRST OF ALL, STOP *SHOUTING*. NOBODY PAID YOU TO KILL MY EARDRUMS...
SECONDLY, WE'VE **BOTH** DONE SOME BAD THINGS. YOU ALMOST SHOT ME, I PUT A BIG OL' STAIN ON YOUR REPUTATION - WATER UNDER THE BRIDGE!

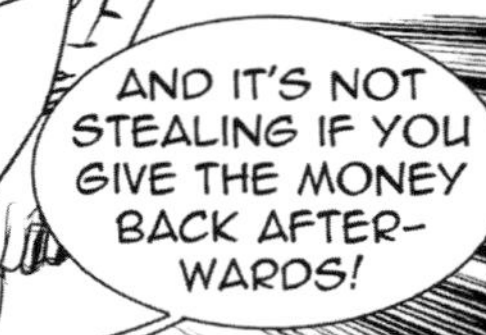
AND IT'S NOT STEALING IF YOU GIVE THE MONEY BACK AFTER-WARDS!

THE FACT IS, SHARPSHOOTER, WE WORK WELL TOGETHER. DAMN WELL.

AND AS IT HAPPENS, I HAVE A LOT OF MONEY THIS TIME...

...***THAT*** SWEETENED YOUR MOOD.

I KNOW YOU'LL WANT IN, ALL THE BIG PLAYERS ARE INVOLVED, AND I'M THE ONLY ONE WHO KNOWS WHAT'S GOING ON.
BUT YOU WON'T SEE A PENNY UNTIL YOU PUT THAT GUN OF YOURS TO GOOD USE.
AND BEFORE YOU CAN DO THAT, WE NEED TO MEET UP.
OH, NOW YOU'VE GOT ME ALL *EXCITED!*
ALRIGHT. WE'LL MEET, BUT NO PROMISES. *YOU* MIGHT NOT WALK AWAY.

100
TEABAGS

HE'S GOOD ISN'T HE?
IF YOU CONSIDER *STEALING* GOOD.
IT'S ONLY THE ESSENTIALS.
TEA IS AN ESSENTIAL ITEM?
IF YOU DON'T CONSIDER TEA ESSENTIAL WE CAN'T BE FRIENDS.
WELL I EXPECTED MORE FROM SOMEONE AS CONSCIENTIOUS AS *KAI*.
HE ***HATES*** IT....
...BUT EVEN KAI HAS TO EAT.
WAS IT SO TERRIBLE TO HOPE YOU'D BRING SOME CASH WITH YOU?
THAT'S WHY YOU SAVED ME?!
STOP LETTING HIM RILE YOU OLIVER!

IT'S OLI, PLEASE. ONLY MY PARENTS AND CREEPY SERIAL KILLERS CALL ME OLIVER.
WHY DO YOU STILL LIVE WITH YOUR PARENTS WHEN YOU'RE 20?
WHAT? THERE'S NOTHING WRONG WITH THAT!
YOU'RE NOT VERY INDEPENDENT ARE YOU?
HE'S NEVER HAD A GIRLFRIEND EITHER.
HOW DID YOU HEAR THAT??
WHAT, IT'S TRUE? DAMN.
YOU GUYS ARE JUST RUDE. A LOT OF PEOPLE LIVE WITH THEIR PARENTS AT 20.
AND YOU KNOW, IT COULD BE WORSE!
AT LEAST I'M NOT HUNG UP ON SOME PSYCHO MURDERER BITCH!
CRAP! DOES HE GIVE EVERYBODY THESE DEATH GLARES?!
NOT ME... CAN YOU SAY SORRY?
I DON'T WANNA TRAVEL WITH THAT...

YOU RIP ME TO SHREDS AND IT'S FINE, I SAY ONE THING AND IT'S LIKE I KILLED YOUR PET...
WE'VE GOT COMPANY!
WHERE?
JUST ONE GUY. HE HAS A SABRE SYMBOL ON HIS NECK. DOESN'T SEEM AWARE OF OUR PRESENCE BUT I WOULDN'T TAKE IT FOR GRANTED.
IF HE SPOTS LEO THERE MIGHT BE TROUBLE.
BZZZZT!
LEO, YOU'VE GOT COMPANY. MAKE YOUR WAY BACK QUICKLY AND QUIETLY

SWEET
SWEET
HEY!

THIEF!
STOP HIM!

I SAID QUIETLY DAMMIT!

KAI! I WAS FINE!
KAI...
KAI KUGO?
JIN KUGO'S SON?
GET IN THE CAR LEO.
QUICK AS YOU CAN.

LEO!
ARE YOU ALRIGHT?
YEAH. HERE'S THAT NOTEBOOK YOU ASKED FOR.
WHERE'S KAI?

DAMN.
WHAT? IS HE OK?
SLAM

UM, WHAT EXACTLY DID HE DO TO THAT GUY?
I'VE DECIDED TO ERASE IT FROM MY MEMORY...
...BUT REMIND ME NOT TO PISS HIM OFF.
UM... RATHER THAN SKIRTING AROUND THE EDGES OF THE CITY...
SHOULDN'T WE JUST LEAVE?
NOOOOOOO...
NUH -UH.
NO WAY.
THE BORDERS ARE REALLY TOUGH TO GET THROUGH.
WHEN WE TRIED TO LEAVE BEFORE IT TOOK SO LONG THAT THOSE RICH GUYS CAME RIGHT UP ON OUR TAIL. KAI GOT SHOT! IT WAS A CLOSE CALL.
I HATE TO BREAK IT TO YA, BUT IN THE GRAND SCHEME OF THINGS WE'RE PRETTY INSIGNIFICANT.
SO IF WE CAN'T LEAVE THE CITY AND CAN'T FIGHT OUR WAY OUT, HOW DO WE GET OUT OF THIS?

WHATEVER'S ACTUALLY GOING ON IS A LOT BIGGER THAN US, THE BEST WE CAN HOPE FOR IS TO SURVIVE IT.
WE WAIT FOR WHOEVER STARTED THIS TO FINISH IT.
YOU MEAN, THIS IS HAPPENING TO US BECAUSE OF SOMETHING GOING ON BETWEEN HIGHER POWERS?
I SUPPOSE. AND SOMEHOW WE'VE BECOME AN OBSTACLE TO THEM ALL.
"SOMEHOW".
JUST LIKE "SOMEHOW" YOU CAN AFFORD TO RUN AN EXPENSIVE CAR AND HIRE AN ASSISTANT BUT CAN'T AFFORD TO EAT. HOW EXACTLY DOES THAT WORK?
I SAVED YOUR LIFE.
MIND YOUR OWN BUSINESS.
MOOOODYYY!

TAKE EVERYTHING RIGHT TO THE BACK
THAT'LL MAKE IT TRICKY TO MAKE AN ESCAPE WHEN THE TIME COMES.
I KNOW, BUT WE HAVE TO REST WHILE WE CAN. WE'LL PLAN OUR ESCAPE ONCE WE'RE SETTLED. I'LL HAVE A LOOK INSIDE.
WAIT FOR ME!

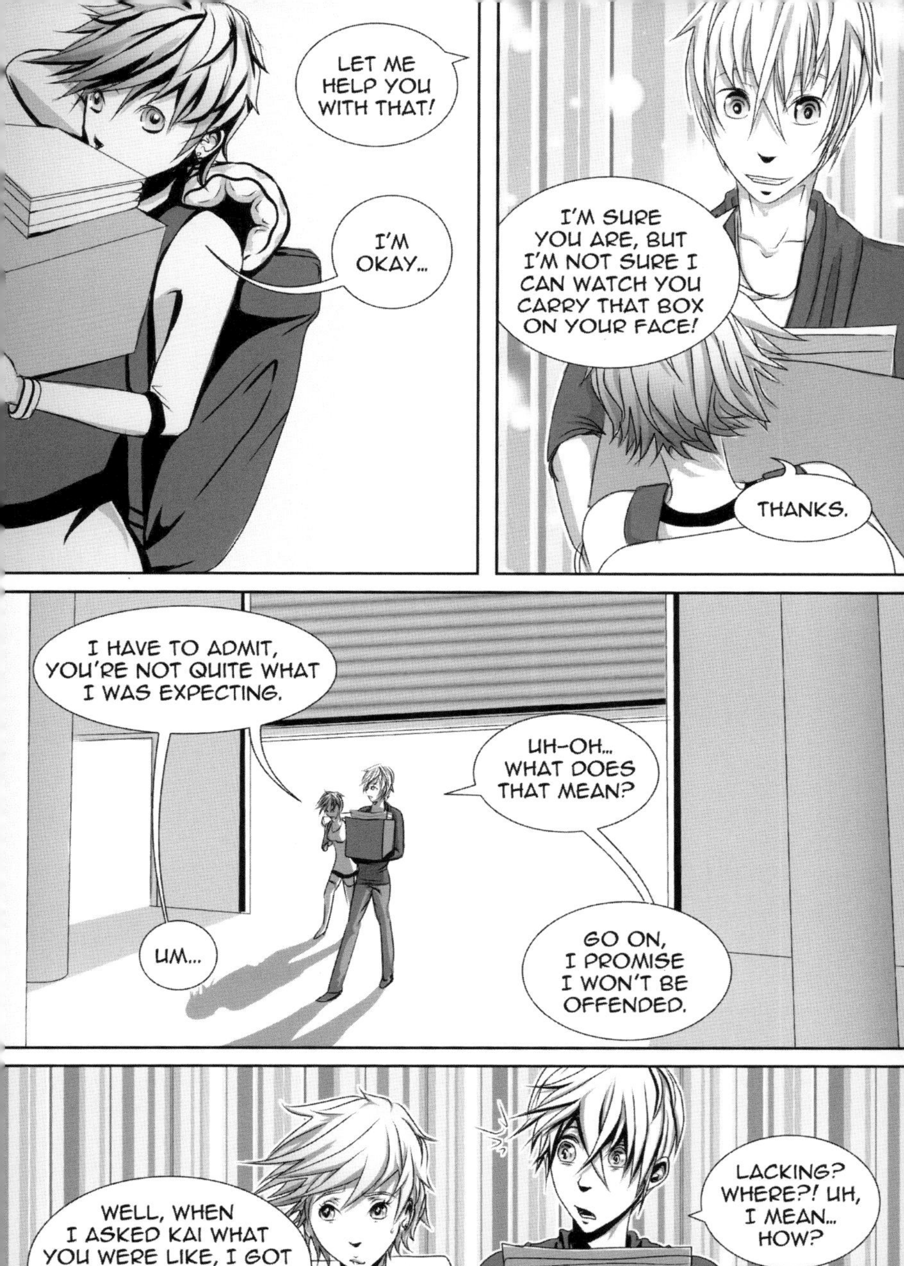
LET ME HELP YOU WITH THAT!
I'M OKAY...
I'M SURE YOU ARE, BUT I'M NOT SURE I CAN WATCH YOU CARRY THAT BOX ON YOUR FACE!
THANKS.
I HAVE TO ADMIT, YOU'RE NOT QUITE WHAT I WAS EXPECTING.
UM...
UH-OH... WHAT DOES THAT MEAN?
GO ON, I PROMISE I WON'T BE OFFENDED.
WELL, WHEN I ASKED KAI WHAT YOU WERE LIKE, I GOT THE IMPRESSION YOU WERE... A LITTLE LACKING...
LACKING? WHERE?! UH, I MEAN... HOW?

I THINK HIS EXACT WORDS WERE "HE'S ALRIGHT IN SMALL DOSES, BUT TENDS TO LOWER THE IQ OF THE WHOLE ROOM."
OUCH!
HIS WORDS! NOT MINE! AND YOU SAID YOU WOULDN'T BE OFFENDED!
BUT THAT'S JUST RUDE!
IF IT COUNTS FOR ANYTHING, I DISAGREE.
REALLY? YOU MUST BE THAT PERSON MY MOTHER KEEPS TELLING ME ABOUT.
HUH?
"THE DAY SOMEONE COMES ALONG WHO CAN TOLERATE YOU IN A CONVERSATION, HOLD ON TIGHT AND DON'T LET GO"
ONE OF HER FAVOURITE PHRASES.
WOW.
OF COURSE HER REAL FAVOURITE PHRASE IS...
OLIVERRR!!!

HATE TO SAY IT, BUT THAT'S NOT A PHRASE!
WELL THEN, I GUESS I'M LIVING UP TO MY REPUTATION.
HEY, SMOOTH TALKER, ARE YOU QUITE DONE OR DO YOU PLAN ON BUYING HER A DRINK AND A MEAL TOO?
THIS GUY...
HE'S JUST STRESSED OUT. HE HAS BEEN ON THE RUN FOR FOUR YEARS.
LIKE THE LONE WOLF! ON THE RUN, TAKING ON THE WORLD!
OH LEE, YOU HAVE A VERY ACTIVE IMAGINATION.
IT'S LEO!!

DOES IT REALLY MATTER?
I DON'T LIKE THAT NAME!
WHY NOT?
WHEN I HEAR THAT NAME I REMEMBER THINGS ABOUT MYSELF THAT I WISH WEREN'T TRUE.
SURELY IT'S NOT THAT BAD...
DOWNTOWN BRINGS OUT THE MONSTERS IN PEOPLE.
I KNOW, BUT YOU GOT OUT. YOU'RE DIFFERENT!
I RAN AWAY, BUT THAT DOESN'T CHANGE THE FACT I'M A MONSTER.
HUH?

BEFORE YOU KNOW IT YOU'VE GOT A GUN AND SOME GUY IN FRONT OF YOU SAYING YOUR NAME....
LEE... LEE PUT IT DOWN, LET ME OFF JUST THIS ONCE!
LITTLE BRO, PLEASE. YOU DON'T HAVE TO DO THIS!
BUT YOU THINK YOU DO, BECAUSE THEY SAY IF YOU DON'T YOU'LL DIE. I DON'T WANNA DIE..
HE SHOULDN'T HAVE JOINED SKYLARK... OR I SHOULDN'T HAVE JOINED RAVEN. WE GOT SEPARATED AND THEN...

BANG.
...WHAT?
I KILLED MY BROTHER.
I'D DO ANYTHING TO BRING HIM BACK. OR JUST TO FORGET.
I'D RATHER DIE THAN REMEMBER WHAT I DID, BUT KAI SAYS I SHOULD TRY AGAIN, AS LONG AS WHAT I'M TRYING TO DO IS GOOD.
THAT'S WHY I DON'T LIKE "LEE".

DOWNTOWN CHANGES PEOPLE.
ONE DAY YOU FIND YOURSELF HOLDING A KNIFE TO SOMEONE'S THROAT AND YOU JUST THINK "HOW DID I GET LIKE THIS?"
I WATCHED HER BECOME NIGHTSHADE, SLOWLY, PAINFULLY AND I DIDN'T STOP IT. NOW I SEE THE SAME THING HAP-PENING AGAIN OLIVER, IN YOU!
DOWNTOWN BRINGS OUT THE MONSTERS IN PEOPLE.
DOWNTOWN IS HELL.

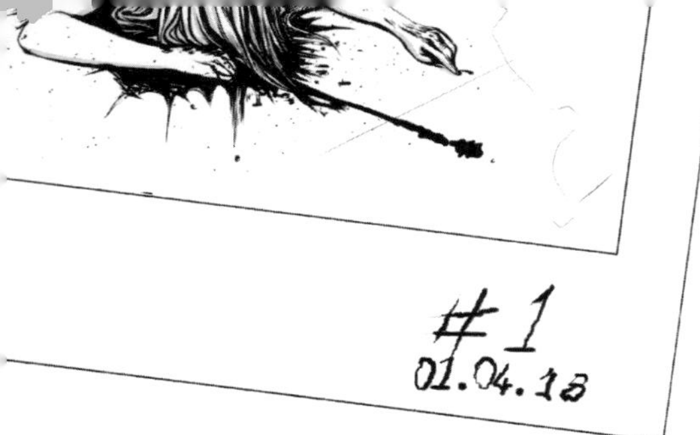

NIGHTSHADE
IS
AUTHORITY.

#2
08.04.18

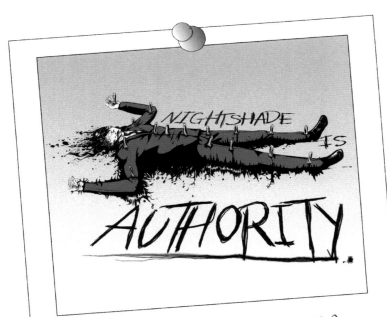

CHARACTER PROFILE

FULL NAME:
BELLA MATSUI
KNOWN AS: NIGHTSHADE
AGE: 22
HEIGHT: 5FT 9IN

BELLA WAS BORN AND RAISED IN A MANSION LOCATED ON MAPLE BOULEVARD IN UPTOWN ASPEN, UNTIL 2007 (AGED 11 YEARS OLD), WHEN HER FATHER DIED IN A FIRE, WHICH WAS A DELIBERATE MURDER PLANNED AND CONDUCTED BY HIDEAKI SUZUKI. BELLA WITNESSED HER FATHER'S CHARRED BODY BEING REMOVED FROM THE BUILDING AND FROM THIS POINT ON SHE AND HER MOTHER WERE FORCED TO LIVE DOWNTOWN; THIS WAS WHEN SHE BECAME FRIENDS WITH KAI KUGO.

TWO YEARS AFTER MOVING DOWNTOWN, HER MOTHER WAS ATTACKED AND KILLED BY TWO SABRE MEMBERS AND BELLA DISCOVERED HER BODY AFTER THREE DAYS OF SEARCHING WITH KAI'S HELP. SHE WOULD LATER TRACK DOWN AND KILL THE INDIVIDUALS RESPONSIBLE FOR BOTH HER PARENT'S DEATHS. THESE EVENTS INSPIRED A HATRED TOWARDS THE IGNORANCE OF THE WEALTHY AND A RESILIENCE AGAINST THOSE WHO TRIED TO TAKE FROM HER, SWEARING SHE WOULD NOT BE BROKEN BY THE VIOLENCE OF OTHERS, WHICH WOULD CONTRIBUTE TO HER FUTURE ACTIONS IN THE NAME OF NIGHTSHADE.

IN MORE RECENT YEARS HER PERSONALITY HAS UNDERGONE SEVERAL CHANGES, ALTHOUGH IT IS IMPORTANT TO NOTE THAT SHE ALSO HAS AN APTITUDE FOR CONCEALLING HER TRUE MOTIVES. IN STRIKE 2 WE SEE BELLA FOR THE FIRST TIME ACTING WITHOUT CONCERN FOR HER IDENTITY, AND THUS SHE DEMONSTRATES A FAR MORE VICIOUS AND CALCULATING SIDE. HER GOALS ARE AS YET UNCLEAR, BUT WITH OVER A YEAR OF PREPARATION BEHIND HER, IT SEEMS WE WILL SEE THEM COME TO FRUITION SOON ENOUGH.

CHARACTER PROFILE

FULL NAME: JIN KUGO
KNOWN AS: KUGO
AGE: 41
HEIGHT: 6FT 6IN

KUGO IS AS DARK-HEARTED AS THEY COME. COLD AND EMOTIONLESS, HE WILL KILL ANYONE HE DEEMS A TRAITOR TO THE BROTHERHOOD, AND THOUGH THE BROTHERHOOD DISBANDED MANY YEARS AGO, HIS VIEW IS THAT IT STILL EXISTS WITHIN RAVEN'S GANG. KUGO HAS VERY LITTLE RESPECT FOR ANYONE OTHER THAN THOSE HE CONSIDERS HIS COMERADES, AND WILL USE OR DISPOSE OF PEOPLE AS HE SEES FIT. ANALYTICALLY, ONE MIGHT SAY HE PICKED A SAW AS HIS WEAPON OF CHOICE BECAUSE OF THE FEAR IT INVOKES OR THE MESSY, AGONIZING IMPACT, BUT IN REALITY, HE JUST LIKES TO FEEL LIKE HE'S REALLY FINISHED HIS JOB BY THE TIME IT'S DONE.

KUGO IS A SYMBOL OF FEAR DOWNTOWN, EVEN TO THE STRONGEST MEMBERS OF SOCIETY AND RIGHTLY SO. ASIDE FROM HIS COMPLETE AND UTTER LACK OF COMPASSION, HE IS FORMIDABLY POWERFUL; HE HAS BEEN KNOWN TO PLOUGH THROUGH ENEMIES AS IF THEY WERE BOWLING PINS, AND HE MAKES SAWING LIVING FLESH AND BONE LOOK LIKE SLIDING A HOT KNIFE THROUGH BUTTER. THERE ARE MANY REASONS TO FEAR KUGO, BUT ONLY ONE RESPONSE TO KNOWING HE IS COMING FOR YOU; RUN.

CHAPTER 4: KILLER CREDENTIALS

YOU'RE BRAVE.
NAH. JUST CONFIDENT.
IT WOULD TAKE A TOTAL OF THREE SECONDS TO HAVE YOU OUT COLD ON THE PAVEMENT.
THREE WHOLE SECONDS? YOU MUST BE LOSING YOUR TOUCH.
THE WALKER I KNEW CERTAINLY WOULDN'T GIVE A WARNING BEFORE A KILL.
NICE TO HAVE YOU BACK.
REALLY? I DIDN'T HAVE YOU DOWN AS THE FORGIVING TYPE.
ADD SIX INCH HEELS AND MILLIONS OF POUNDS TO A MIND LIKE YOURS AND ANYTHING IS POSSIBLE.
I'LL BEAR THAT IN MIND.

HOW WAS PRISON?
A LOT LIKE DOWNTOWN IN SOME WAYS, MORE DANGEROUS IN OTHERS, BUT ULTIMATELY QUITE RESTRICTIVE.
I THINK YOU'LL FIND THAT'S THE POINT.
ANYWAY, I HEAR YOU'VE COME INTO A CONSIDERABLE SUM OF MONEY...
HOWEVER, YOU *DID* MAKE USE OF MY SERVICES FREE OF CHARGE FOR A CONSIDERABLE LENGTH OF TIME, AND THEN CAST THE BLAME ONTO ME FOR SABRE'S DEATH!
IN MY DEFENCE, WALKER, YOU *DID* BLAST THE CONTENTS OF THE MAN'S SKULL ACROSS HIS LIVING ROOM FLOOR.
YES, WE DID HAVE SOME FUN. YOU'D HAVE BEEN MY FAVORITE CLIENT IF ONLY YOU PAID...
DETAILS.
STILL, I'LL HAVE YOU KNOW I LIKED SABRE, AND IT WAS MOSTLY YOUR FAULT.
I HAVE EVERY RIGHT TO GOUGE YOU FOR THE SERVICES YOU'VE TAKEN THE LIBERTY OF SAMPLING.

HA. HONESTLY, IF SOMEONE HADN'T PILFERED HALF OF IT AWAY ON A FANCY CAR AND A PERT LITTLE ASSISTANT I WOULDN'T BEGRUDGE YOU A DAMN THING.
WHAT HAPPENED TO HIM?

HE BECAME TOO...

...DULL.

DULL ENOUGH TO WANT DEAD?

ALL IN GOOD TIME!
YOU REALLY ARE PROACTIVE TODAY!

DON'T WORRY.
I HAVE PLENTY OF WORK FOR YOU. I STILL HAVE - AS YOU SO TACTFULLY PUT IT - A "CONSIDERABLE SUM"...
...BUT FIRST...
TALK TO ME ABOUT ANTONIO BALESTERO MASOMILIO.
POLITICIANS ARE BORING.

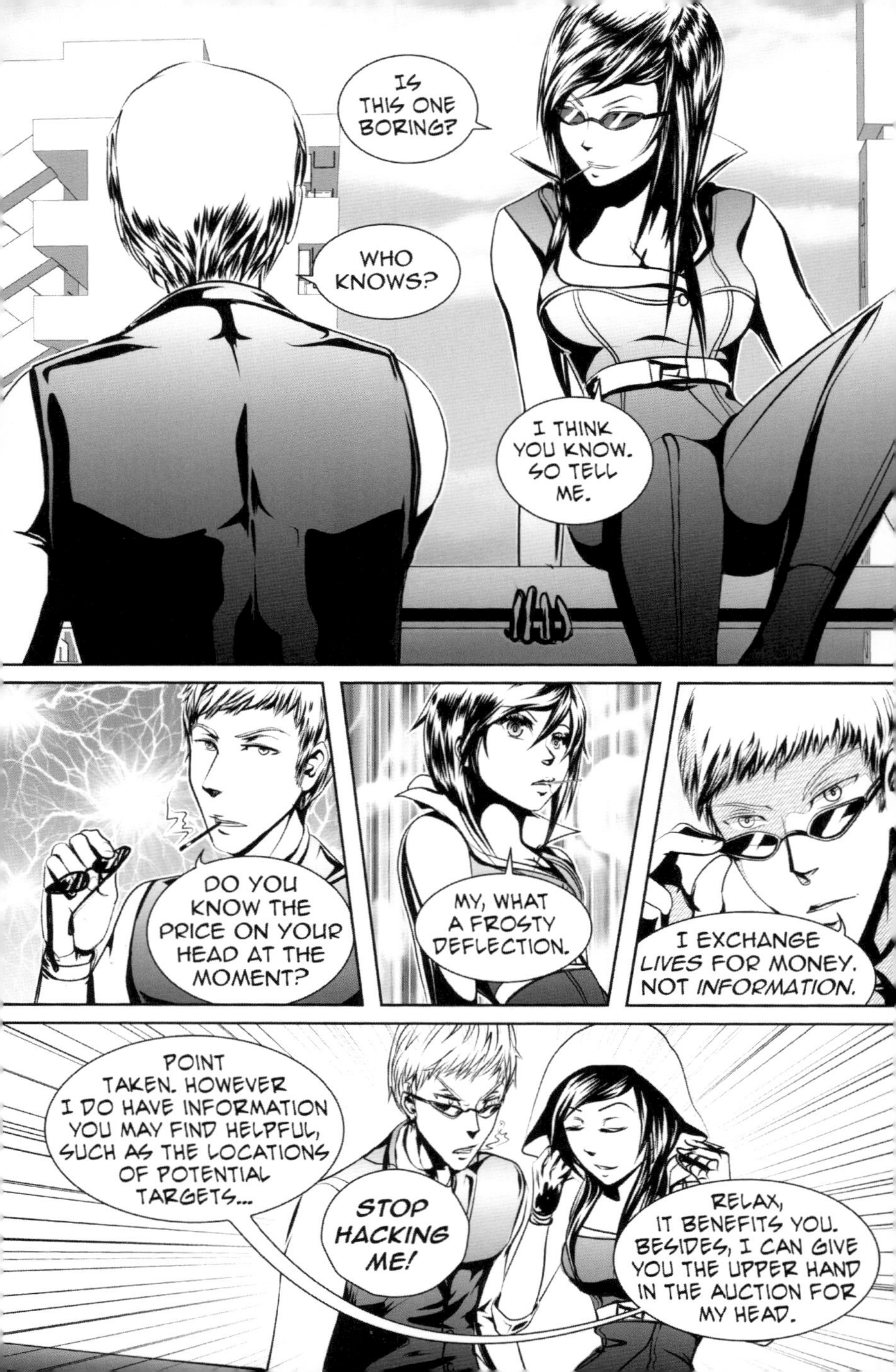
IS THIS ONE BORING?
WHO KNOWS?
I THINK YOU KNOW. SO TELL ME.
DO YOU KNOW THE PRICE ON YOUR HEAD AT THE MOMENT?
MY, WHAT A FROSTY DEFLECTION.
I EXCHANGE *LIVES* FOR MONEY. NOT *INFORMATION*.
POINT TAKEN. HOWEVER I DO HAVE INFORMATION YOU MAY FIND HELPFUL, SUCH AS THE LOCATIONS OF POTENTIAL TARGETS...
STOP HACKING ME!
RELAX, IT BENEFITS YOU. BESIDES, I CAN GIVE YOU THE UPPER HAND IN THE AUCTION FOR MY HEAD.

HM?

YOU HAVE AN APARTMENT UPTOWN, DON'T YOU?

YES.

OH, I SEE.

ALRIGHT. BUT IF YOU WANT TO STAY WITH ME, YOU'LL HAVE TO FOLLOW *MY* RULES.
SURE, YOU CAN TRUST ME.
TRUST YOU? *HAH.* NO. BUT IT IS A BIT LIKE TRUST, I CAN SHOOT YOU WHENEVER I PLEASE.
THAT'LL DO.

Blue Diamond
HI ANTON.
HEY LEMALA! HOW'S THINGS?
STILL STRESSED, BUT GOOD. I HAVE A MEETING WITH THE BOSS TODAY; CAN'T SAY I'M NOT A LITTLE NERVOUS.
BOSS? YOU MEAN, THE BIG BOSS?
YEAH, MASOMILIO. BEN ALWAYS USED TO HANDLE THIS STUFF, I'LL NEVER GET USED TO IT.

THAT'S GREAT, YOU'RE GOING UP IN THE WORLD! THERE'S NO NEED TO BE NERVOUS.
ARE YOU TELLING ME YOU *WOULDN'T* BE NERVOUS IF YOU WERE CALLED INTO A MEETING WITH SOMEONE WHO COULD END YOUR CAREER WITH A FLICK OF HIS WRIST?
I'M SAYING YOU SURVIVED BEING THE HOSTAGE OF A PYRO-MANIAC GANGSTER BOSS AND YOU'RE NERVOUS ABOUT MEETING A POLITICIAN.
I SUPPOSE I WOULD BE A LITTLE MORE CONCERNED IF I HAD A MEETING WITH SKYLARK.
I KNOW WHAT YOU NEED. YOU NEED TO SPEAK TO THE BIG MAN.
HEY ASARE, DO YOU WANT TO SAY HELLO TO AUNTY LEMALA?
WAIT, NO ANTON, DON'T! I'M ABOUT TO GO INTO MY MEETING!
ANTON?
LELALAA!

. . .
LELALA!
LELALA!
MISS ADEWA?
LELALA!
LELALA!

SOUNDS LIKE AN IMPORTANT CALL. DO JOIN ME WHEN YOU ARE QUITE READY.
I'M DONE.

RED OR WHITE?
WHITE PLEASE.
NOW, I TAKE IT YOU HAVE HEARD ABOUT NIGHTSHADE?
WHAT ABOUT HER?
SHE HAS ESCAPED FROM PRISON.
MY APOLOGIES, I THOUGHT YOU HAD BEEN INFORMED.

ESCAPED?

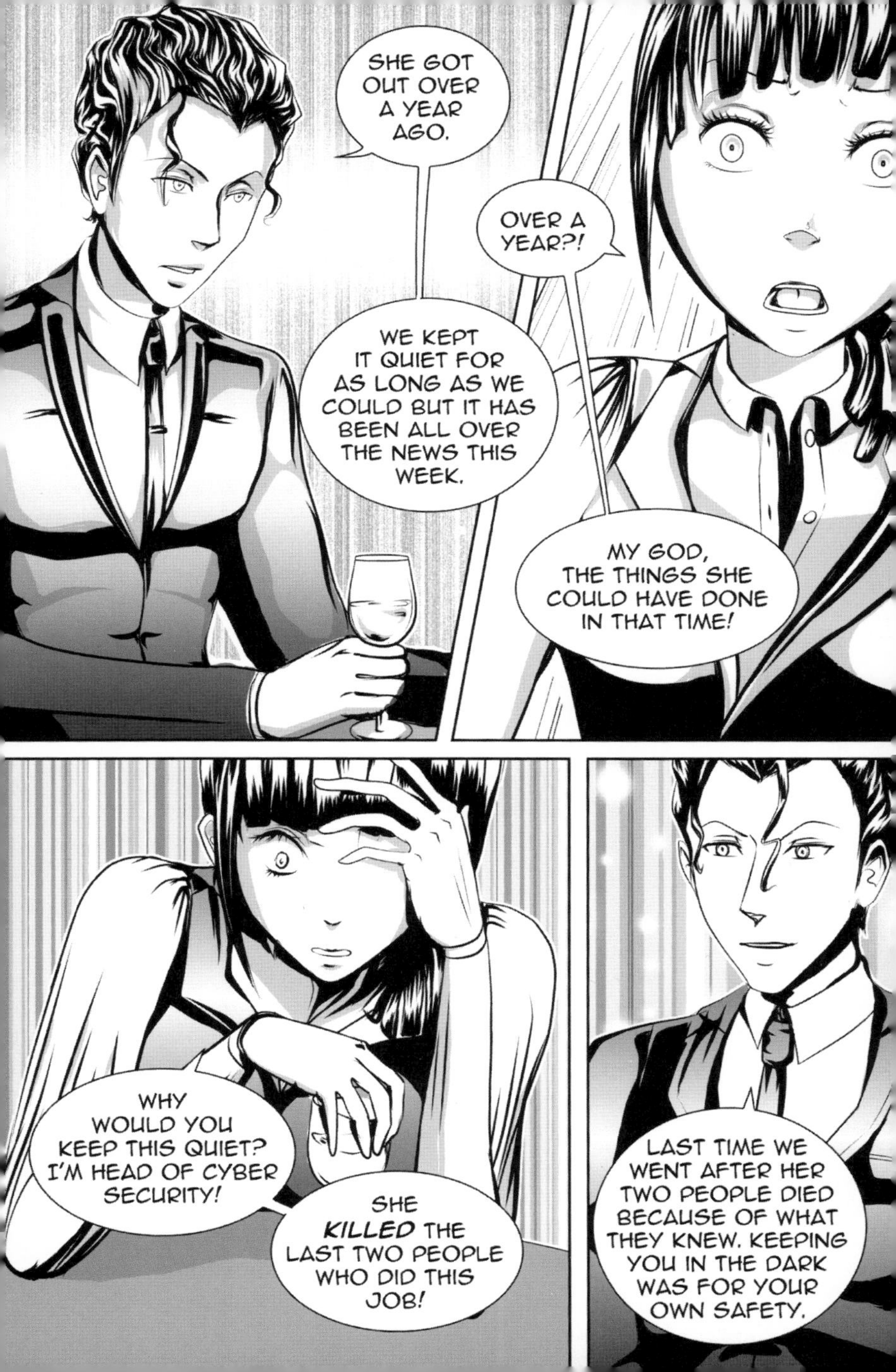

SHE GOT OUT OVER A YEAR AGO.
OVER A YEAR?!
WE KEPT IT QUIET FOR AS LONG AS WE COULD BUT IT HAS BEEN ALL OVER THE NEWS THIS WEEK.
MY GOD, THE THINGS SHE COULD HAVE DONE IN THAT TIME!

YOU DON'T UNDERSTAND. BEFORE SHE WAS ARRESTED, I... I HELPED OLIVER SLOANE LEAK HER IDENTITY. AND... I KNEW IT WAS LIKELY TO GET HER KILLED.
YOU DID THAT?
SHE WILL COME FOR ME, I KNOW IT.
NO. YOU ARE IN MY CITY NOW AND I WILL NOT LET HER HURT YOU.
THAT'S WHY WE'RE HERE TODAY. I HAVEN'T BEEN SITTING AROUND WAITING FOR HER TO STRIKE; I HAVE BEEN WORKING TOO, ON STOPPING HER.
I WOULD LIKE YOU TO TAKE A LOOK AT THIS.

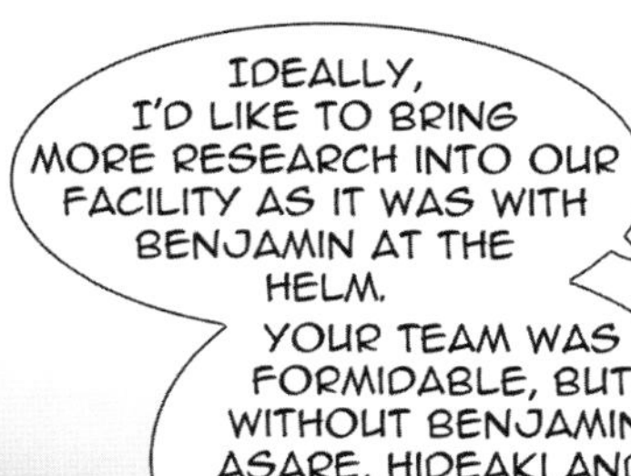
IDEALLY, I'D LIKE TO BRING MORE RESEARCH INTO OUR FACILITY AS IT WAS WITH BENJAMIN AT THE HELM.
YOUR TEAM WAS FORMIDABLE, BUT WITHOUT BENJAMIN, ASARE, HIDEAKI AND MASAO IT'S ASKING RATHER A LOT FROM YOU.

SO HOW WOULD YOU FEEL ABOUT WORKING LIKE THIS?
WITH EXTERNAL GROUNDWORK? THIS IS IMPRESSIVE STUFF, BUT WOULDN'T IT BE BETTER TO INVITE THEM TO WORK IN-HOUSE?

UNFORTUNATELY, THAT IS NOT POSSIBLE.

WHAT A SHAME. THIS REMINDS ME OF THE SORT OF THING MASAO USED TO CHALK UP.

THEN I CAN LEAVE IT WITH YOU AND TRUST YOU KNOW WHERE TO GO WITH IT?

YES, IT WOULD BE MY PLEASURE SIR.
FANTASTIC.
AH, SIR! I NEED TO SPEAK TO YOU!
CLAUDIA, HAVEN'T YOU FINISHED WITH THOSE FILES YET? IT REALLY SHOULDN'T TAKE THIS LONG.

UHM, IT'S BECAUSE THERE'S SOMETHING THAT CONCERNS ME, SIR.

WHAT CONCERNS YOU MY DEAR?

IT'S THIS PRISONER-
NAME?
KUGO. YOU'VE SIGNED THE RELEASE FORM.
AND WHY DOES THAT CONCERN YOU?

WELL, HE WAS ARRESTED FOR PUBLICLY DISMEMBERING A MAN WITH A SAW. WHEN QUESTIONED, HE SAID...
"THE BASTARD TURNED AGAINST HIS BROTHERS AND I'LL PUNISH EVERY LAST ONE OF THEM" AND THEN, UH, SOME OTHER THINGS THAT I PROBABLY SHOULDN'T REPEAT.

IF YOU DISLIKE THE MAN'S LANGUAGE THEN PLEASE REFRAIN FROM POLLUTING MY OFFICE WITH IT.
AND DO TRY TO REMEMBER THAT YOU ARE MY ASSISTANT, NOT MY ADVISOR.

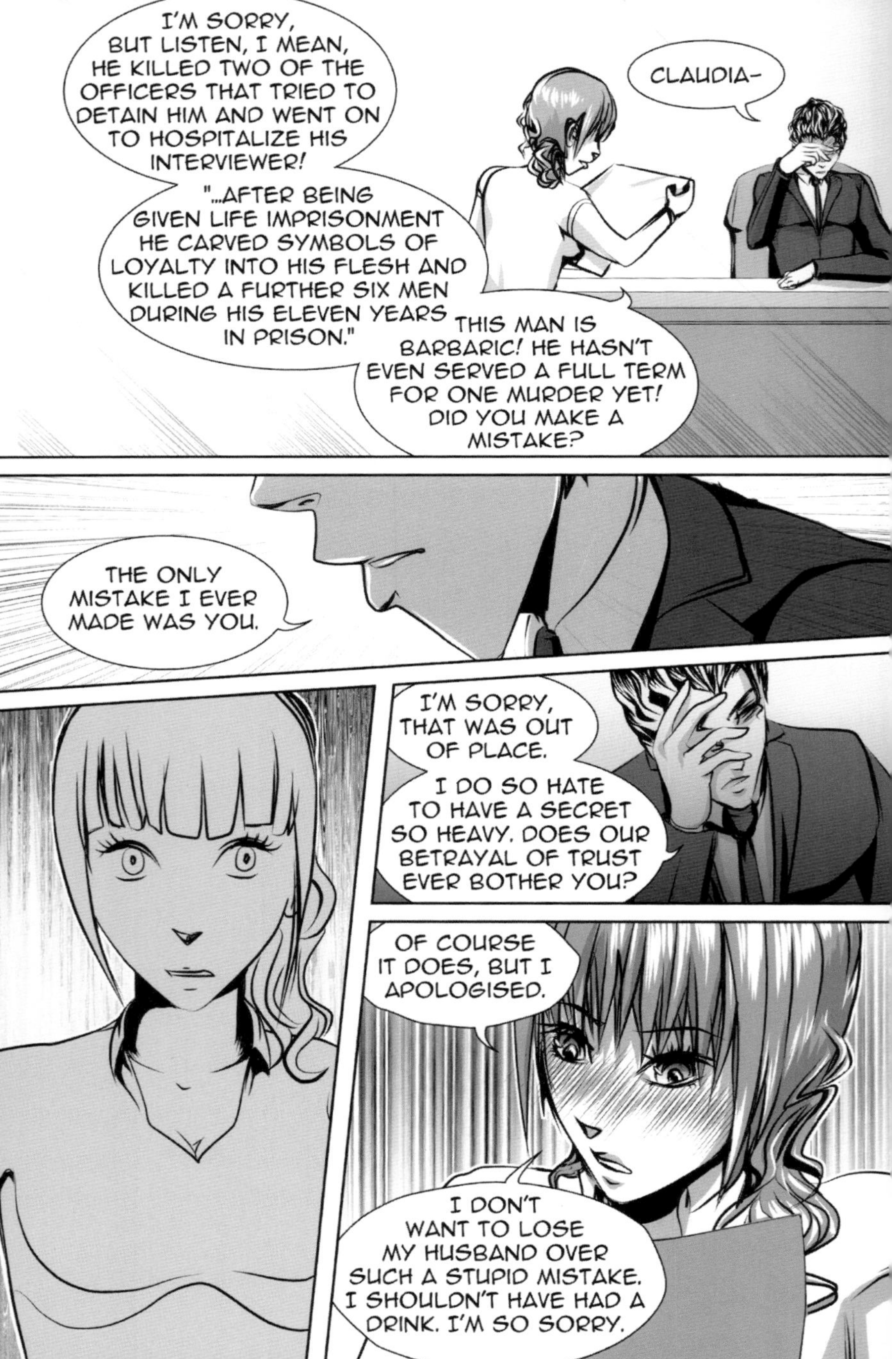
I'M SORRY, BUT LISTEN, I MEAN, HE KILLED TWO OF THE OFFICERS THAT TRIED TO DETAIN HIM AND WENT ON TO HOSPITALIZE HIS INTERVIEWER!
"...AFTER BEING GIVEN LIFE IMPRISONMENT HE CARVED SYMBOLS OF LOYALTY INTO HIS FLESH AND KILLED A FURTHER SIX MEN DURING HIS ELEVEN YEARS IN PRISON."
CLAUDIA-
THIS MAN IS BARBARIC! HE HASN'T EVEN SERVED A FULL TERM FOR ONE MURDER YET! DID YOU MAKE A MISTAKE?
THE ONLY MISTAKE I EVER MADE WAS YOU.
I'M SORRY, THAT WAS OUT OF PLACE.
I DO SO HATE TO HAVE A SECRET SO HEAVY. DOES OUR BETRAYAL OF TRUST EVER BOTHER YOU?
OF COURSE IT DOES, BUT I APOLOGISED.
I DON'T WANT TO LOSE MY HUSBAND OVER SUCH A STUPID MISTAKE. I SHOULDN'T HAVE HAD A DRINK. I'M SO SORRY.

YOU'RE RIGHT. TO DESTROY WHAT WE LOVE BY CONFESSING TO SUCH A SILLY MISTAKE WOULD BE FOOLISH, WOULDN'T IT?
I SUPPOSE I'LL HAVE TO FIND ANOTHER WAY OF MAKING PEACE WITH MY CONSCIENCE.
SORRY. I REALLY AM.
FELICIA, DARLING? HOW ARE YOU? OH, ME? I'M FINE. STRESSFUL DAY, VERY... STRESSFUL. BUT IT'S GOOD TO HEAR YOUR VOICE!
WHAT COULD HAVE POSSESSED ME TO DO SUCH A TERRIBLE THING?

I'M HUNGRY!
YOU EAT TOO MUCH!
I'M A GROWING MAN.
YOU'RE NOT EVEN HUNGRY, YOU'RE JUST BORED.
WELL WHAT ELSE IS THERE TO DO? I'M SO BORED HIDING IN OLD BUILDINGS ALL THE TIME.
WE'RE NOT ON HOLIDAY YOU KNOW. WHAT DO YOU USUALLY DO FOR FUN?
PLAY GAMES OR WATCH ANIME.
IS THAT ALL?
WHAT'S WRONG WITH THAT?
NOTHING PER SE, BUT IN THIS SITUATION THERE ARE OTHER THINGS TO APPRECIATE.
YOU COULD SOCIALISE, FOR EXAMPLE.

SOCIALIZING IS OVER-RATED.
I AM RIGHT HERE YOU KNOW; WE CAN TALK ABOUT ANYTHING YOU LIKE. YOU MIGHT EVEN ENJOY IT.
HM.
DID I DO SOMETHING WRONG?
YOU THINK I'M STUPID.
I REALLY DON'T!
WHEN YOU MEET NEW PEOPLE YOU HAVE A CHOICE; SHARE YOUR HEART WITH THEM OR HAVE A LAUGH.
IF YOU SHARE YOUR HEART WITH SOMEONE YOU OPEN YOURSELF UP TO BEING HURT, SO ACTING THE FOOL IS A MUCH SIMPLER WAY TO BE.
WHO HURT YOU?
WELL... I DID GET VERY CLOSE TO A GIRL ONCE, CLOSER THAN I'D EVER BEEN WITH ANYBODY, AND NOT ONLY DID SHE NOT RETURN MY FEELINGS...

SHE LIED TO ME AND HURT MY FAMILY, BETRAYING ME IN EVERY WAY YOU CAN THINK OF.
SOUNDS LIKE SHE HAS A LOT TO ANSWER FOR, BUT NOT EVERYONE IS LIKE THAT.
I KNOW. OR AT LEAST, I THINK I DO, BUT I'VE NEVER BEEN ABLE TO LOOK AT PEOPLE THE SAME WAY SINCE.
EVEN IF I TRY NOT TO, MY BRAIN IS CONSTANTLY TRYING TO FIGURE OUT HOW SOMEONE MIGHT HURT ME.
I HATE BEING ALONE, BUT TRYING TO BE WITH OTHER PEOPLE IS SO EXHAUSTING NOW.
AND SOMEHOW... EVEN THOUGH WE'RE BEING CHASED BY PEOPLE WITH GUNS, I FEEL GOOD.
BECAUSE I'M NOT ALONE.
I UNDERSTAND COMPLETELY.
REALLY?

IT IS NOT A DESIRE FOR ATTENTION, BUT A NEED FOR APPROVAL AND REASSURANCE. TO KNOW THAT YOUR LIFE HAS WORTH, BUT AT THE SAME TIME, YOU ARE TOO AFRAID TO HAND OVER THE REQUIRED TRUST FOR THAT SORT OF FRIENDSHIP.
IF YOU HAVE LEARNED ANYTHING FROM WHAT HAPPENED, YOU SHOULD KNOW BETTER THAN TO ASSUME YOU KNOW WHAT I DO AND DO NOT UNDERSTAND.
I WAS WITH THIS GUY ONCE... SORT OF.
HE MADE ME FEEL VALUED, SPECIAL... IMPORTANT. I GAVE HIM EVERYTHING AND HE...
ARE YOU OK?
I THINK I SEE NOW THAT THE WAY HE TREATED ME WASN'T RIGHT...
BUT EVEN NOW, THERE'S STILL THIS POWER HE HAS OVER ME... IT JUST... HURTS.

THAT MAKES ME ANGRY.
A PERSON WHO KNOWINGLY ABUSES A PERSON'S FEELINGS TO MANIPULATE THEM IS JUST AS BAD AS A PERSON WHO USES VIOLENCE.
WHY?
IT'S HEARTLESS TO WILLINGLY HURT SOMEONE EVEN IF IT ISN'T PHYSICAL. IT JUST HURTS ME TO KNOW THAT SOMEBODY HURT YOU.
IT'S NOT LIKE I'M CLEAR OF BLAME, WE JUST DIDN'T SEE THINGS THE SAME WAY. I MISUNDERSTOOD.
BUT IF HE LET YOU MISUNDERSTAND THAT ISN'T OK.
YOU'RE WORTH MORE THAN THAT! IF I EVEN HAD A SHOT WITH SOMEONE LIKE YOU, I'D NEVER TREAT YOU THAT WAY. MY CONSCIENCE WOULDN'T LET ME.
AND BESIDES, YOU'RE THE KIND OF PERSON THAT SHOULD BE HELD ONTO, NOT THROWN AWAY. I HOPE THAT AT LEAST MAKES YOU REALIZE THAT YOU ARE VALUABLE.

SO ARE YOU.

SERIOUSLY, WHEN DID YOU BECOME SUCH A SMOOTH TALKER?
SMOOTH? WAS THAT SMOOTH?
RING RING

WHERE'S THAT COMING FROM?

RING
RING

RING
RING

RING
RING

SHOULD WE ANSWER IT?

...I GUESS NOT THEN.
RING RING

YOU THERE, BOY?

KAI?!

#1
01.04.18

NIGHTSHADE
IS
AUTHORITY.
#2
08.04.18

NIGHTSHADE
CONTROLS.
#3
15.04.18

THE RISE OF NIGHTSHADE

EARLY YEARS:

THE IDEA OF NIGHTSHADE WAS FIRST CONCEIVED BY 13-YEAR-OLD BELLA MATSUI AS AN ESCAPIST FANTASY FOR HER DIFFICULT CIRCUMSTANCES.
THE FIRST TIME NIGHTSHADE WAS MENTIONED BY ANYONE ELSE WAS AFTER AN INCIDENT THAT INVOLVED YOUNG BELLA USING THE NAME TO ESCAPE MUGGERS. HER ATTEMPT FAILED, BUT IN AN UNRELATED INCIDENT ONE OF THE ASSAILANTS DIED, AND THE OTHER REMEMBERED THE NAME. IN A CHILDISH ATTEMPT TO GET SOME REVENGE ON HER ATTACKERS BELLA PUT TOGETHER A RUDIMENTARY DEVICE FOR DISTORTING HER VOICE AND USED IT TO PRANK CALL THE MUGGER, USING THE NAME "NIGHTSHADE" AS A PSEUDONYM.
AS TIME WENT ON BELLA BEGAN EXPERIMENTING WITH THE IDEA, THREATENING THOSE SHE FELT THREATENED BY IN ORDER TO MAKE HER OWN LIFE EASIER, BUT EVENTUALLY THE CHARADE HIT AN INEVITABLE SNAG AS SHE REACHED TOO HIGH AND THREATENED RAVEN, WHO RIGHTLY CHALLENGED HER POWER.
IT WAS AT THIS POINT, AT THE AGE OF 15, THAT SHE FIRST BEGAN USING THE NAME IN ORDER TO MANIPULATE PEOPLE TO HARM OTHERS. IT WAS NOT, HOWEVER, UNTIL A YEAR LATER, THAT SHE KILLED ANYONE.

DEVELOPMENT:

IT IS WELL KNOWN AT THIS POINT THAT AT THE AGE OF 16, BENJAMIN SLOANE SOUGHT OUT BELLA, AND IN A PANIC, SHE KILLED HIM. WHAT IS NOT SO WELL DOCUMENTED IS WHY HE SOUGHT HER OUT.
BELLA'S FATHER WAS AN EXCEPTIONAL CRYPTOGRAPHER FROM JAPAN, SOUGHT OUT BY MASOMILIO, AND HIRED AS PART OF A TEAM TO PUSH THE BOUNDARIES OF COMPUTER SECURITY. WHEN HE DIED HIS MONEY AND BELONGINGS WENT TO HIDEAKI SUZUKI, WHO HAD FORGED HIS WILL, LEAVING THE FAMILY DESTITUTE. ALL BELLA HAD WAS HER FATHER'S RESEARCH AND PERSONAL EFFECTS. NOT KNOWING THAT THIS RESEARCH AND EQUIPMENT WAS HIGHLY CONFIDENTIAL, BELLA HAD STUDIED AND MADE USE OF IT IN HER NIGHTSHADE ACTIVITIES. THUS, BENJAMIN SLOANE CAME TO TAKE IT BACK. UNTIL THIS POINT, NIGHTSHADE HADN'T BEEN MORE THAN AN URBAN LEGEND BRUSHED ASIDE BY THOSE IN A POSITION OF POWER, BUT AFTER THIS INCIDENT YOUNG BELLA UNDERWENT A TRANSFORMATION OF CHARACTER THAT WOULD PLACE HER FIRMLY ON THE MAP.

AFTER DISPOSING OF BENJAMIN'S BODY BELLA WENT INTO A DEEP DEPRESSION FOR EIGHT MONTHS, REGRETTING HER ACTIONS AND FEELING DEEPLY PAINED THAT SHE HAD DESTROYED ANY HOPE OF ACHIEVING THE FUTURE SHE HAD DESIRED HER ENTIRE LIFE. THIS DROVE HER TO LOSE SIGHT OF HER HOPES TO ESCAPE DOWNTOWN AND BECOME A RESPECTED CRYPTOGRAPHER. INSTEAD SHE FORCED HERSELF TO SWALLOW DOWN HER CONSCIENCE AND BEGIN DOING WHAT SHE CONSIDERED NECESSARY TO BUILD NIGHTSHADE INTO THE VEHICLE OF HER DESIRES, AND GET WHAT SHE WANTED FROM THE RUINS OF HER LIFE.

THE RISE OF NIGHTSHADE CONT'D.

ROAD TO RUIN:

REALIZING HER OWN INTELLIGENCE, BELLA CAME TO THE CONCLUSION THAT THE MORAL VALUES SHE HAD BEEN TAUGHT WERE THE STUMBLING BLOCKS TO HER SURVIVAL. IN ORDER TO PROTECT HER OWN INTERESTS SHE SET ABOUT STRATEGIZING TO TAKE OVER DOWNTOWN. SHE TOOK SEVERAL MILLIONS OF POUNDS FROM WALKER, AND USED THIS TO MANIPULATE HIM INTO KILLING FOR HER. SHE THEN DISMISSED THE CHALLENGES TO NIGHTSHADE'S ABILITIES BY KILLING SEVERAL RAVEN MEMBER'S AND WOUNDING RAVEN HIMSELF.
AFTER SEVERAL OTHER BOLD MOVES THAT DEMANDED THE ATTENTION AND SUBSERVIENCE OF DOWNTOWN'S AUTHORITY FIGURES, NIGHTSHADE BECAME A HOUSEHOLD NAME, AND A DEEPLY FEARED ONE AT THAT.
DUE TO PERSONAL STRUGGLES OF CONSCIENCE BROUGHT ON BY THE CONCERNS OF HER CLOSEST FRIEND, BELLA LEFT NIGHTSHADE BEHIND FOR A PERIOD OF MONTHS UNTIL OLIVER SLOANE SHOWED UP LOOKING FOR ANSWERS. THIS SPURRED A RELAPSE THAT RESULTED IN THE ASSASSINATION OF AMBROGIO SABRE - A HUGE MOVE BY NIGHTSHADE THAT CLAIMED OWNERSHIP OF DOWNTOWN AND PUSHED BELLA BEYOND THE POINT OF NO RETURN. AMIDST THE PERSONAL INTERNAL CONFLICT THAT ENSUED, THE ESCALATING SITUATION AND GROWING CONCERN FOR HER ANONIMITY, BELLA KILLED AN INNOCENT CIVILIAN FOR THE FIRST TIME; ASARE FULLINGER.
IN 2014 BELLA'S CHARACTER UNDERWENT ITS MOST INTENSIVE CRISIS, AS SHE FACED DECISIONS THAT INVOLVED HER FRIENDS, HER SECRET IDENTITY, HER POWER, AND HER LIFE. SHE DID NOT HANDLE ALL OF THESE THINGS WELL, AND AFTER A MENTAL BREAKDOWN, HER IDENTITY WAS DISCOVERED AND SHE WAS HUNTED BY THE VARIOUS CRIMINALS SHE HAD MANIPULATED. AFTER THIS, BELLA WAS EVENTUALLY ARRESTED AND IMPRISONED.

IMPRISONMENT AND RESURGENCE:

IN PRISON, BELLA WAS GIVEN ACCESS TO PSYCHIATRIC INTERVENTION TO HELP IDENTIFY AND DEAL WITH HER ISSUES, WHICH SHE PURSUED, BUT ONCE AGAIN HER IDENTITY WAS LEAKED AND HER LIFE WAS IN PERIL ONCE MORE. FOLLOWING AN ATTACK THAT LEFT HER BEDRIDDEN FOR SIX WEEKS, SHE REFUSED FURTHER AID AND INSTEAD BEGAN TO MAKE PLANS TO ESCAPE PRISON AND PURSUE A NEW GOAL.
AFTER ESCAPING PRISON BELLA DISAPPEARED FOR 13 MONTHS, ALL THE WHILE LAYING FOUNDATIONS FOR HER NEXT OPERATION. SHE RECEIVED SURGERY IN SEPTEMBER, 2017 THAT INVOLVED THE IMPLANTATION OF COMPUTER PARTS INTO HER BODY.

CHALLENGES TO THE TITLE:

IN 2014, KAI MADE A PHONECALL USING NIGHTSHADE'S IDENTITY IN AN ATTEMPT TO SCARE AWAY OLIVER SLOANE AND PREVENT BELLA'S RELAPSE.
A SERIES OF MURDERS TOOK PLACE BETWEEN 1ST APRIL & 13TH MAY 2018 WHICH ALL FEATURE NIGHTSHADE'S NAME, BUT NO RESPONSIBILITY HAS BEEN TAKEN AS YET.
IN THE "PREMONITION" PROLOGUE CHAPTER WE WITNESS AN UNIDENTIFIED CALLER USE THE NAME "NIGHTSHADE" WHILE SPEAKING TO BELLA. THIS EVENT ACTUALLY TAKES PLACE IN A FUTURE CHAPTER OF NIGHTSHADE, LATE 2018 IN THE STORYLINE.

CHAPTER 5: LOYALTY'S BONEYARD

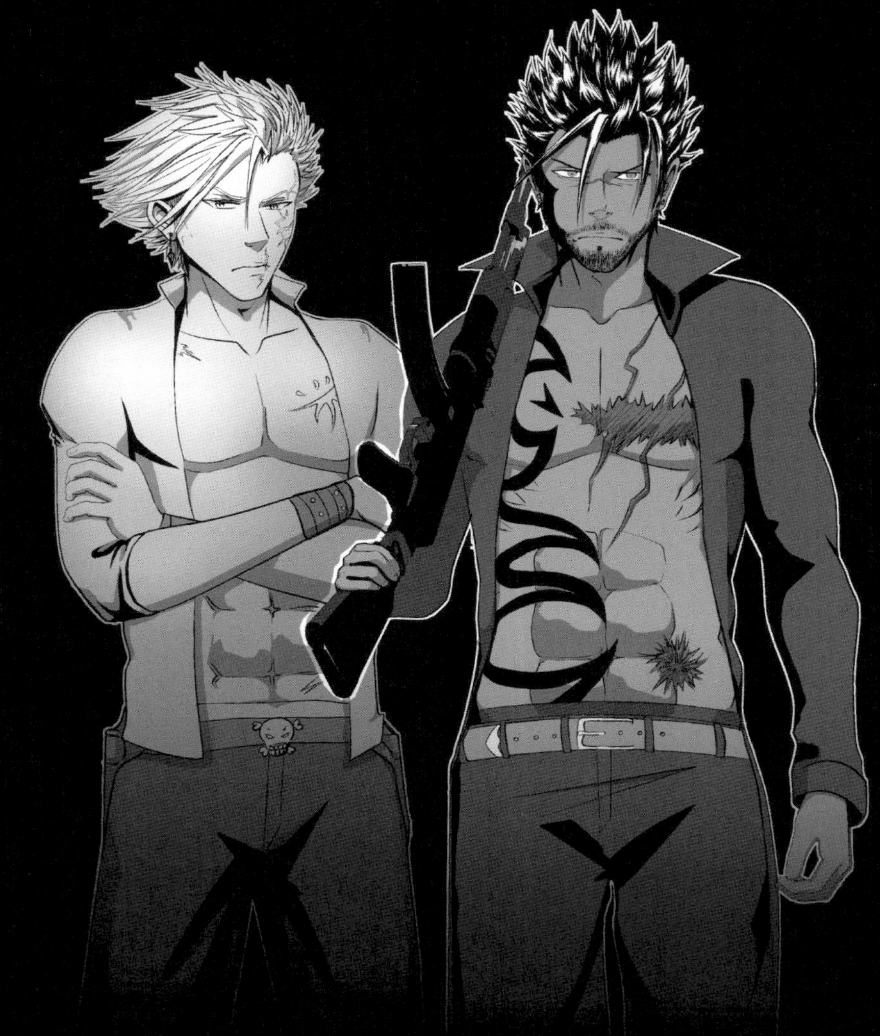

ONE BY ONE...
...GENERATION AFTER GENERATION...
...LIKE A BITTER RITE OF PASSAGE...
...THE CHILDREN OF DOWNTOWN MUST DECIDE HOW THEY ARE GOING TO SURVIVE.
WHETHER THEY CAN AFFORD TO TRUST ONE ANOTHER...
...WHETHER THEY WILL FOLLOW IN THE FOOTSTEPS OF THEIR PREDECESSORS...
...HOW THEY CAN LIVE WITH THE COST OF THEIR ACTIONS...
...HOW THEY CAN COMBAT THE PRECONCEPTIONS THAT MAKE THEM VULNERABLE...
...AND WHAT THEY ARE WILLING TO SACRIFICE IN ORDER TO ENSURE A SAFER FUTURE.

TWO SUCH CHILDREN WERE ONCE SO CLOSE THEY CALLED THEMSELVES BROTHERS.
IN THE ABSENCE OF ANY OTHER FAMILY THEY LOOKED OUT FOR ONE ANOTHER AND CREATED THEIR OWN RULES.
THEY MADE THEIR SUFFERING THEIR STRENGTH AND BECAME FIGUREHEADS FOR OTHERS LIKE THEM.
THEY NAMED THEIR CLOSE-KNIT GROUP "THE BROTHER-HOOD".
COMERADERIE OFFERED COMPANIONSHIP, AND THEIR NO-TOLERANCE REPUTATION EARNED THEM SAFETY. BUT NOT EVERY-ONE COULD STOMACH THIS METHOD OF SURVIVAL.

TAKE ARABELLE, FOR EXAMPLE; BEAUTY, SENSITIVITY AND YOUTH MADE HER AS ADMIRABLE AS THEY DID VULNERABLE.
WHEN HER BEAUTY HAD CAUSED HER ENOUGH PAIN SHE DECIDED NOT TO GIVE HERSELF OVER TO LOVE, BUT TO USE HER BEAUTY TO SECURE A SAFER FUTURE.
SHE SUCCEEDED IN CAPTURING THE HEART OF RUSHIN VALOR, WHO NOW CALLED HIMSELF "SKYLARK"; PROMISING LOVE IN RETURN FOR PROTECTION.
BUT IN TIME IT BECAME MUCH MORE DIFFICULT TO PRETEND, AS SHE FOUND HERSELF FALLING, QUITE GENUINELY, FOR SOME-ONE UNEXPECTED.

WHEN IT BECAME APPARENT THAT HE TOO HARBORED FEELINGS FOR HER, AND KEPT THEM BOTTLED UP FOR THE SAKE OF HIS CLOSEST FRIEND, THINGS BECAME MUCH WORSE.
IT ONLY TOOK ONE SMALL LAPSE OF JUDGE-MENT...
IT FELT RIGHT. IT FELT LIKE FATE. IT FELT LIKE REAL LOVE, THE KIND NEITHER KNEW EXISTED. SOMETHING GOOD WAS HAPPENING FOR THE FIRST TIME IN FOREVER.
IF ONLY SHE HAD FOUND HIM FIRST, PERHAPS THIS TOWN WOULD NOT BE TORN IN HALF.
FLICK
FOR WITH THEIR ACTIONS CAME DIRE, IRREVOCABLE CONSEQUENCES.

RUSHIN!
HOW'S THE BABY?
ANY NEWS?!

WHAT'S WRONG?
IT'S YOURS.

SMASH

MINE?
ROXANNA, MOVE.
NO. BACK OFF.
WHATEVER'S GOING ON BETWEEN YOU DOESN'T JUSTIFY SMASHING YOUR BROTHER'S FACE THROUGH A WINDOW!
NO. I DESERVED THAT.
WHAT THE HELL DID YOU DO?!

ARE YOU SURE IT WAS HIM?
FOR NINE MONTHS YOU LET ME BELIEVE I WAS GOING TO HAVE A FAMILY.
AND WHEN I FINALLY SEE MY SON, IT'S YOURS.
SHE TOLD ME.
GOD JOBI. REALLY?
RUSHIN, I HAD NO IDEA. I'M SO SORRY...
IT WAS JUST THE ONCE, SHE WAS GOING TO LEAVE YOU BUT I STOPPED HER! I THOUGHT IT WAS ALL OVER WHEN YOU TOLD ME SHE WAS HAVING A BABY.

IF YOU'D GIVE ME CHANCE TO SPEAK YOU MIGHT REALISE I'VE SUFFERED OVER THIS ENOUGH ALREADY.
YOU?! SINCE WHEN HAVE *YOU* EVER SUFFERED? ALL YOU DO IS TAKE!
SERIOUSLY?! I COULD HAVE TAKEN HER IF I WANTED TO. I LOVED HER, BUT I GAVE HER UP FOR YOUR SAKE! DO YOU HAVE ANY IDEA HOW HARD THAT WAS?

SHE WAS EVERYTHING I WANTED BUT I LET YOU HAVE HER!
SO I SCREWED UP ONCE, I'M SORRY! BUT IT'S NOTHING NEXT TO HOW MUCH YOU HURT ME BY BEING WITH HER! I HAD TO WATCH AND PRETEND I DIDN'T CARE!
SHE NEVER EVEN LOVED YOU! THAT'S THE WORST PART! SHE WAS JUST TOO SCARED TO LEAVE YOU, BECAUSE YOU WOULD HAVE TURNED ON US BOTH!
BOTH OF YOU, STOP! PLEASE!

I'LL KILL YOU...
I'LL KILL YOU!

YOU'RE GOING TO DESTROY EVERYTHING WE BUILT TOGETHER BECAUSE OF SOMETHING LIKE THIS?
HE DESTROYED EVERYTHING WHEN HE DECIDED TO BETRAY HIS BROTHER FOR A WOMAN!
YOU TOO? WHAT THE HELL?!
YOU'RE GONNA BURN.

BROTHERS...

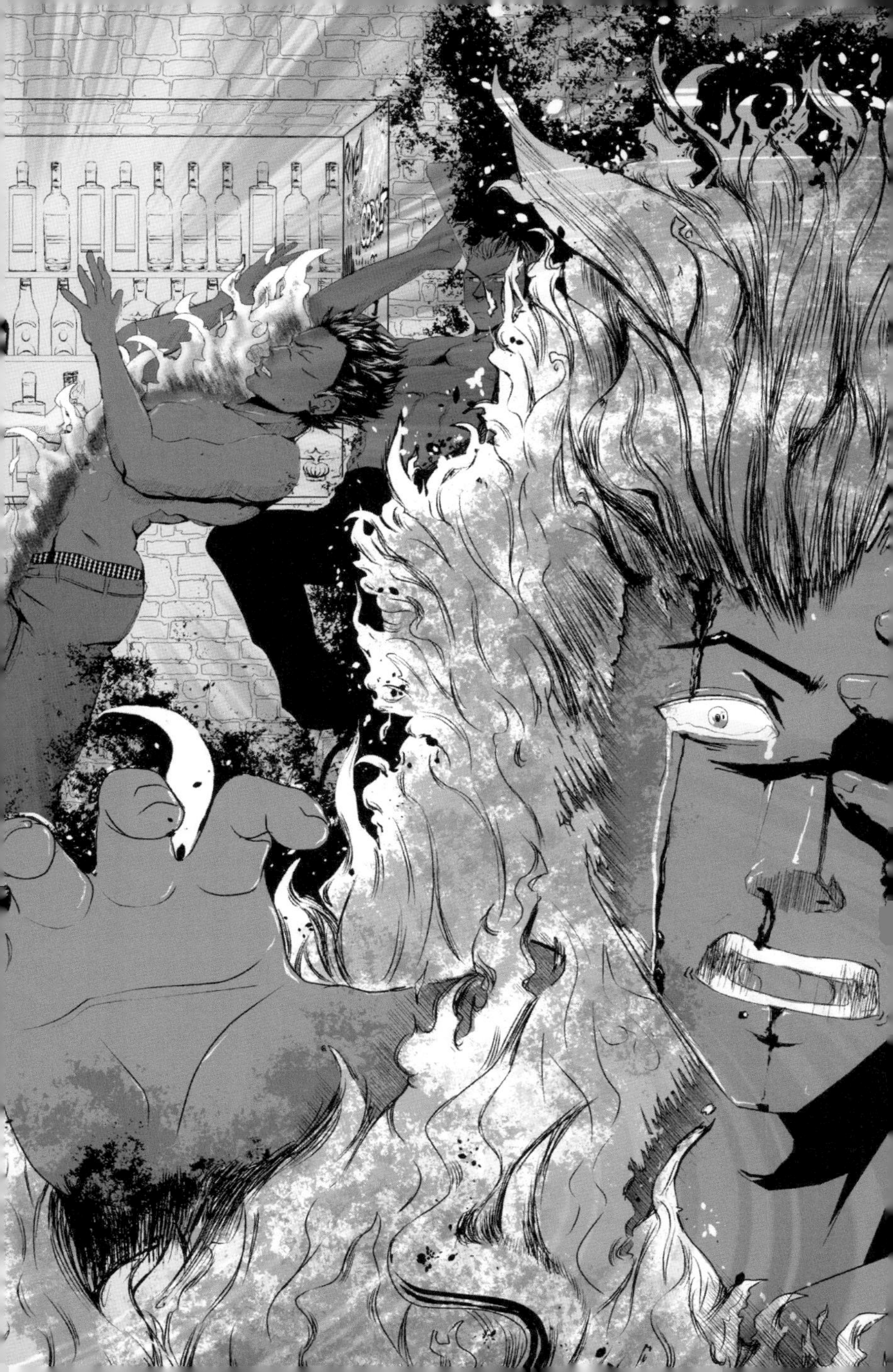

IN A HEARTBEAT EVERYTHING CHANGED. FRIENDS BECAME MORTAL ENEMIES, DRIVEN BY EMOTIONS MORE RAW AND POTENT THAN ANYTHING THEY'D EVER FELT, AND AS THE BROTHERHOOD SHATTERED, SO TOO DID THE MINDS OF THOSE WHO LIVED BY ITS PRINCIPLES.
THE BROTHERHOOD WAS THE ONLY HOPE FOR PEACE IN THIS NIGHTMARE.
WE WORKED FOR YEARS!
WE BLED! WE FOUGHT!
AND YOU... SET YOUR OWN BROTHER ON FIRE?

TRAITORS

KUGO VALUED NOTHING MORE THAN THE BROTHERHOOD...
...AND TO KUGO, IT WAS SKYLARK WHO WAS RESPONSIBLE FOR ITS DESTRUCTION...
...IN HIS MIND, ALL THOSE THAT SIDED WITH SKYLARK WERE TRAITORS, AND MUST BE DESTROYED.
HIS MADNESS WAS WITHOUT FEAR, AND HE CHASED HIS VICTIMS NO MATTER HOW FAR THEY RAN.
AAAAAAAH

WHEN HE FOUND HIMSELF UPTOWN, SURROUNDED BY POLICE, HE SIMPLY CONTINUED SAWING AWAY AT EVERY OBSTACLE; HUMAN OR NOT.
POLICE
POLICE
CAUTION KEEP OUT

CAUTION KEEP OUT
AFTER THE MASSACRE, HE WAS FINALLY SENTENCED TO LIFE IN PRISON.
RAVEN TRIED TO ESCAPE THE MEMORIES.
BUT IT DIDN'T MATTER HOW DEEPLY HE DROWNED HIS SORROWS...
THE ONLY THING THAT MATTERED WAS ARABELLE AND THEIR SON, SAM.
HE SWORE, FOR THEIR SAKE, HE WOULD KILL SKYLARK, AND MAKE A SAFER WORLD FOR HIS CHILD.

...BUT
SHE KNEW
THAT.

SHE HAS TO PAY...

...NIGHTSHADE, KAI, THAT STUPID BLOND KID...
ANYONE WHO EVER ASSOCIATED WITH HER. MAKE THEM ALL PAY.

OH, THEY'LL PAY. YOU CAN COUNT ON THAT.
BB
BB

#1
EVERYTHING.
NIGHTSHADE
#4
22.04.18

TIMELINE: PRE-SEASON ONE

01/09/1982
BENEDICT REDFIELD WALKER IS ELECTED MAYOR OF THE CITY OF ASPEN.

07/02/1983
"DOWNTOWN" IS DISOWNED BY THE GOVERNING AUTHORITIES OF ASPEN CITY.

20/07/1990
MASAO MATSUI AND VALENTINA BELMONTE ARE MARRIED.
06/06/1990
JOBI CLARKE (AKA RAVEN) IS BORN
12/12/1990
RUSHIN VALOR (AKA SKYLARK) IS BORN.

21/12/1992
THE SLOANE FAMILY RELOCATE TO ASPEN CITY.

09/12/1993
A.B.MASOMILIO (AGED 20) FORMS TEAM OF ELITE CRYPTOGRAPHERS.
MASAO MATSUI MOVES TO ASPEN CITY TO WORK FOR MASOMILIO.

01/10/1994
THE SABRE FAMILY SIEZE CONTROL OF DOWNTOWN.

05/08/1995
KAI KUGO IS BORN.

24/07/1996
BELLA MATSUI IS BORN.
05/09/1996
PANZERA, MUNITIONS COMPANY, IS FOUNDED.

20/04/1998
JOHN SLOANE AND LUCY GLADSTONE ARE MARRIED.
01/09/1998
ANTONIO BALESTERO MASOMILIO IS ELECTED MAYOR OF THE CITY OF ASPEN.

14/03/2002
LEILA TASHIRO (KAI'S MOTHER) IS STRANGLED TO DEATH.

01/08/2004
A.B.MASOMILIO MARRIES FELICIA GROSVENOR.

28/08/2005
BENEDICT R. WALKER AND HIS WIFE ARE ASSASSINATED.

2004-2006
THE BROTHERHOOD RISES TO POWER DOWNTOWN.

24/07/2007
MASAO MATSUI DIES IN A FIRE IN HIS WORKPLACE.
10/10/2007
SAM CLARKE IS BORN.
10/10/2007
THE BROTHERHOOD SPLITS.
01/11/2007
JIN KUGO IS ARRESTED FOR THE MURDER OF MULTIPLE POLICE OFFICERS.

25/05/2008
THE GANGS "RAVEN" AND "SKYLARK" ARE FORMED, AND THE BROTHERHOOD'S OLD TERRITORY IS SPLIT INTO TWO WARRING ZONES.

15/11/2009
VALENTINA MATSUI DIES FOLLOWING A MUGGING DOWNTOWN.

22/02/2012
BENJAMIN SLOANE IS SHOT DEAD.
2012-2013
NIGHTSHADE RISES TO POWER.

TIMELINE: SEASON ONE ONWARDS

02/05/2014
OLIVER SLOANE HEADS DOWNTOWN IN ORDER TO INVESTIGATE NIGHTSHADE.
29/05/2014
AMBROGIO SABRE IS ASSASSINATED UNDER NIGHTSHADE'S ORDERS.
13/06/2014
RAVEN ATTACKS BELLA. HE REMOVES THE THIRD AND FOURTH FINGERS ON HER LEFT HAND.
22/06/2014
HIDEAKI SUZUKI IS DISMEMBERED BY SHAR AS ORDERED BY NIGHTSHADE.
23/06/2014
ASARE FULLINGER IS SHOT DEAD BY NIGHTSHADE AFTER UNCOVERING THEIR IDENTITY.
29/06/2014
BELLA (STILL ANONYMOUS AS NIGHTSHADE) STABS KAI WITH A KITCHEN KNIFE.
11/07/2014
OLI DISCOVER'S NIGHTSHADE'S IDENTITY AND LEAKS IT LEADING TO DOWNTOWN'S INFAMOUS "NIGHT OF SCARS". KAI BETRAYS HIS ALLEGIEANCE TO HIS GANG AND BECOMES A TARGET OF RAVEN.
12/07/2014
BELLA IS HOSPITALISED AND PLACED UNDER ARREST. HER POSSESSIONS ARE SEIZED AND PASSED ON TO MASOMILIO.

03/03/2015
BELLA PLEADS GUILTY TO MURDER AND MANSLAUGHTER AND IS SENTENCED TO TEN YEARS IN PRISON.
08/04/2015
KAI VISITS BELLA IN PRISON FOR THE LAST TIME. BELLA PASSES ON A MEMORY CARD LABELLED "HIDEAKI".
25/07/2015
BELLA IS MOVED TO HM ASPEN HIGH SECURITY PRISON FACILITY.
07/06/2015
RAVEN REUNITES WITH ARABELLE. THEY DISCUSS REIGNITING THEIR RELATIONSHIP AND HE IS ALLOWED TO SEE HIS SON FREQUENTLY.
16/10/2015
BELLA IS ATTACKED BY PRISON INMATES, SUFFERING A SERIOUS ABDOMINAL WOUND.

18/08/2016
LEO JOINS KAI.
10/10/2016
BELLA ESCAPES PRISON, KILLING FIVE INMATES, TWO GUARDS AND HER PSYCHIATRIST.

01/08/2017
CALLIE JOINS KAI & LEO.
26/09/2017
JONATHAN WALKER PERFORMS A MYSTERY OPERATION ON BELLA.
16/11/2017
BELLA/NIGHTSHADE DISCONNECTS THE ENTIRE CITY OF ASPEN'S ELECTRICITY AND DATA NETWORKS AND MAKES CONTACT WITH MASOMILIO, DEMANDING HIS COOPERATION AND THREATENING HIS FAMILY AND ALL-OUT WAR BETWEEN UPTOWN AND DOWNTOWN IF HE REFUSES.

TIMELINE: SEASON TWO

18/03/2018
OLIVER SLOANE IS APPROACHED BY UNIDENTIFIED MEN IN SUITS AND THEN KIDNAPPED BY KAI, CALLIE AND LEO. HE JOINS THEM ON THE RUN AVOIDING DETECTION FROM VARIOUS ENEMIES WHO WANT THEM DEAD.
29/03/2018
KUGO IS RELEASED FROM PRISON.

AUTHOR'S NOTE

ANOTHER VOLUME OF NIGHTSHADE COMPLETE, AND WHAT A JOURNEY IT HAS BEEN! EVER SINCE THE END OF SEASON ONE I HAVE BEEN WORKING FULL TIME AS AN ARTIST ON VARIOUS MANGA AND COMIC SERIES, WHICH HAS BEEN FANTASTIC. I TOOK A YEAR AWAY FROM NIGHTSHADE TO IMPROVE MY ARTISTIC SKILLS, AND I HOPE IT SHOWS! THOUGH THERE HAVE BEEN MANY REAL OBSTACLES ALONG THE WAY, I DID IT, OR RATHER, WE DID IT; BECAUSE WITHOUT THE SUPPORT OF FRIENDS, FANS, FAMILY AND PATRONS WE WOULDN'T BE HERE. THANK YOU FOR SUPPORTING ME. THANK YOU MOST OF ALL FOR LOVING THE SERIES, BECAUSE IF I WAS THE ONLY ONE MAD ABOUT THIS STORY IT WOULD BE A SAD STATE OF AFFAIRS... AND I AM NOW MORE EXCITED THAN EVER ABOUT NIGHTSHADE!

IT TOOK TWO YEARS TO MAKE THIS BOOK, FOR A NUMBER OF REASONS. STARTING OUT AS A FREELANCE ARTIST WAS PRECARIOUS FINANCIALLY, BUT THINGS ARE GETTING BETTER AND BETTER AS TIME GOES ON, WHICH MEANS I PULL BACK A LITTLE MORE TIME TO SPEND ON NIGHTSHADE EVERY MONTH. AND NATURALLY, THE OLDER I GET THE MORE RESPONSIBILITIES (AND EXPENSES... LIFE, EH?) I HAVE.
MY DREAM IS THAT IN TIME I WILL BE ABLE TO DEVOTE MY TIME SOLELY TO MY OWN WORKS, AND LIKE A CLICHE SHONEN PROTAGONIST, I WILL KEEP TRYING UNTIL THAT BECOMES A REALITY! THERE IS A LOT I WANT TO CREATE, WHICH INCLUDES ANOTHER SIX VOLUMES OF NIGHTSHADE, BUT GOES FAR BEYOND THAT. I HAVE BEGUN REMASTERING THE FIRST SERIES OF NIGHTSHADE TO BRING IT UP TO SCRATCH WITH MY RECENT WORK, BUT THAT'S A SLOW PROCESS SINCE NEW CONTENT HAS TO COME FIRST.

LASTLY, 200 HOURS ALONE IN THE OFFICE FOR EACH CHAPTER WOULD GET VERY LONELY WITHOUT THE COMMENTS AND MESSAGES YOU SEND ME ALL THE TIME, SO THANKS FOR KEEPING ME GOING, AND I WOULD LOVE FOR YOU TO JOIN ME ON THE REST OF MY JOURNEY! :)

I AM...
@HANNARRAWR *ON TWITTER*
@HANNAROSEPRO *ON INSTAGRAM*
@NIGHTSHADEMANGA *&* ***@HANNAROSEARTIST*** *ON FACEBOOK*
HANNA ROSE *ON PATREON*
MIREROSE *ON DEVIANTART*

KEEP IN TOUCH! X

Hanna Rose x